C000170910

Other Titles of Interest

EASY PC INTERFACING

by

R. A. PENFOLD

BERNARD BABANI (publishing) LTD
THE GRAMPIANS
SHEPHERDS BUSH ROAD
LONDON W6 7NF
ENGLAND

Please Note

Although every care has been taken with the production of this book to ensure that any projects, designs, modifications and/or programs, etc., contained herewith, operate in a correct and safe manner and also that any components specified are normally available in Great Britain, the Publishers do not accept responsibility in any way for the failure, including fault in design, of any project, design, modification or program to work correctly or to cause damage to any other equipment that it may be connected to or used in conjunction with, or in respect of any other damage or injury that may be so caused, nor do the Publishers accept responsibility in any way for the failure to obtain specified components.

Notice is also given that if equipment that is still under warranty is modified in any way or used or connected with home-built equipment then that warranty may be void.

First Published – November 1995

British Library Cataloguing in Publication Data
Penfold, R. A.
  Easy PC Interfacing
  I. Title
  004.616

  ISBN 0 85934 385 5

Printed and bound in Great Britain by Cox & Wyman Ltd, Reading

Preface

The IBM PCs and compatibles are now the dominant computers in virtually every aspect of micro computing. This includes the domain of do-it-yourself add-ons for computers, where PCs have been steadily taking over from the eight bit computers that were once so popular for this type of thing. In fairness to the better eight bit computers, it has to be said that they remain an excellent basis for do-it-yourself hardware add-ons. However, as more and more of the 8 bit machines fall into obsolescence, modern 16 bit alternatives have to be sought out. The PCs are the obvious choice.

I think it is true to say that most of today's 16 and 32 bit computers are not well suited to operation with user add-ons. They were simply not designed with this type of thing in mind, and in most cases have very limited potential for this type of expansion. The PCs are much more accommodating due to their expansion slots, which make it easy to add special interfaces (home constructed or otherwise). Unfortunately, interfacing to the expansion bus requires very accurately made custom printed circuit boards, and producing these is not an easy do-it-yourself task.

The PCs have no built-in user port of the type found on some eight bit computers, but many PCs have an unused printer port which will actually work quite well as a sort of pseudo user port. A PC printer port has five input lines and no less than 12 output lines. With some simple external hardware the number of input and output lines is easily boosted. This makes it easy to interface a wide range of user add-ons to a PC printer port. In most cases there is no need to use a double-sided printed circuit board, and many printer port add-ons can actually be constructed on a proprietary circuit board such as stripboard. The PC joystick port is more limited in its capabilities, but its four digital inputs and four resistance reading analogue inputs have some potential in general interfacing applications.

The circuits featured in Chapter 1 of this book provide some analogue and digital input/output ports. These are then used with the projects featured in Chapter 2. The projects cover a range of sensing, measurement, and control applications. It is assumed that the reader has at least a basic knowledge of PC programming and electronics, but it is not essential to be an expert in either field. Neither is it necessary to have an advanced PC in order to use the projects. They should work properly with any PC from an original 4.77MHz 8088 type, to the latest super-fast machines. The only requirement is a spare printer port, or in a few cases a "games" port is required.

R. A. Penfold

Contents

Chapter 1

INS AND OUTS

The IBM PCs and compatibles are the nearest thing to a standard computer for use in the home, office, laboratory, etc. Probably the main reason for the popularity of these computers is their versatility. Most PCs have at least two or three spare expansion slots which can take all sorts of weird and wonderful add-on cards, such as parallel interface boards and analogue to digital converter cards. In addition to the ready-made add-ons, interfacing your own projects to the PC expansion bus is perfectly possible. This topic is covered in two books from the same publisher and author as this book ("Interfacing PCs And Compatibles" (BP272), and "Electronic Projects For Your PC" (BP320)).

While it has to be admitted that interfacing direct onto the PC expansion bus is in many ways the best approach, it is also slightly awkward. It requires the use of custom printed circuit boards which must be accurately made (and of the double-sided variety), or projects based on proprietary prototyping cards. This second method is relatively straightforward, but it does not necessarily produce a very neat finished product, and the prototyping cards are not particularly cheap.

So is there a simpler way of connecting user add-ons to a PC? I suppose that this is a "how long is a piece of string?" style question. With some types of add-on circuit there is probably no realistic alternative to using the expansion slots. For example, if vast numbers of input/output lines are required, either a custom interface card must be produced, or your add-on must interface via a ready-made multi-line interface card. With many of the more simple and straightforward projects though, the standard PC ports often offer a practical (and easier) alternative to the expansion bus.

Printer Port

There are three types of standard PC port that are potentially usable for your own add-ons. These are the serial, parallel, and analogue ports. Interfacing via a serial port is not particularly difficult, and the serial-to-parallel and parallel-to-serial conversion is easily achieved using a UART (universal asynchronous receiver/transmitter). However, in this book we will not consider the serial ports for general purpose interfacing, simply because it is normally easier to use the parallel printer ports. Obviously most PCs have a printer port connected to a printer, and this port is therefore unavailable for general use unless you resort to some form of "printer sharer" switching device. On the other hand, many PCs have a second printer port, and in most cases this is left totally unused. Even if a second port is not fitted, a very inexpensive expansion card is all that is needed in order to equip your computer with a second port.

Although a printer port may seem to be a bit limited for general interfacing purposes, the PC printer ports are actually quite versatile. On the face of it a parallel printer port is an output type, and it has little or no potential for use as an input port. Fortunately, in addition to the eight data outputs a PC printer port has several handshake lines. In fact there are no less than nine of these – five inputs and four outputs. As we shall see later in this chapter, the handshake lines enable the port to act as an input or output type, or both at once.

Some external circuitry is required in order to make the port function as an 8 bit input type, but it only requires a very simple and inexpensive add-on. Obtaining eight input and eight output lines using one of the printer ports is certainly much easier than using a serial port or the expansion bus to provide the same function. Also, the parallel port can read and write at a much higher rate, and it still has some spare lines for general handshaking purposes or other uses. One possible use for these extra lines is to provide further 8 bit input or output ports. It is actually possible to obtain a large number of input and output lines using a printer port and basic multiplexing techniques. For complex interfacing of this type I would be inclined to opt for a proper multi-port expansion card, but the printer port method is perfectly feasible if that is the approach you prefer.

Joystick Port

Most PCs seem to be supplied complete with a "games" port, which is primarily intended for use of joysticks of the type which contain two potentiometers, and not switch type joysticks. With the latter the user can only indicate that an on-screen object should move in a particular direction (up, down, left, right, or a combination of two adjacent directions). With a potentiometer style joystick the user indicates a particular screen position for the controlled object. There are two potentiometers in the joystick which provide X (horizontal) and Y (vertical) positions. From the general interfacing point of view an input port intended for use with potentiometer joy-sticks is of more value than one intended for use with switch joysticks. An input port that can read the settings of poten-tiometers is an analogue type which, on the face of it, has numerous practical applications.

Unfortunately, the "games" port of a PC is a rather basic form of analogue port. It does not really compare to (say) the 12 bit voltage reading port of the BBC machines. It is actually more akin to the "paddle" inputs on the Commodore/Atari type joystick port. It responds directly to the resistance of the poten-tiometer, rather than having the potentiometer's track connect-ed across the supply lines and then reading the wiper voltage. The general scheme of things seems to be to have the poten-tiometer in a simple C – R timing circuit. At the beginning of a timing cycle a software routine starts counting upwards from zero. When the charge voltage on the capacitor reaches a cer-tain value a "flag" in the interface changes state, and indicates to the software routine that the count must be halted. The high-er the resistance of the potentiometer, the longer it takes for the charge voltage to be reached, and the higher the count produced by the software routine.

In theory it is possible to obtain a high degree of linearity with this system. In practice it usually seems to provide quite poor linearity, and is not usually up to the task of accurate measurement. As implemented in a typical PC "games" port there is a definite lack of linearity. Of course, this non-linearity is not important in the port's intended application, but it renders it of relatively little value as a general purpose analogue port. There is a further problem in that the port reads resistance rather than voltage, but most signal sources will provide a varying voltage not a varying resistance. This makes it necessary to read most sensors via a voltage-to-resistance circuit, which is a difficult form of conversion, and one that is

3

likely to further impair the linearity of the system. Consequently, the analogue inputs of the games port are not really suitable for precise measurement, but they can be used in non-demanding applications to read sensors such as thermistors and cadmium sulphide photocells.

The PC joystick ports do not only have analogue inputs, and there are also some digital inputs. These are included as a means of reading the "fire-buttons" of the joysticks, but they are usable as general purpose digital inputs. With its simple analogue inputs, limited number of digital inputs, and no digital outputs at all, the analogue port is clearly of comparatively limited value as a general purpose port. Consequently, in this book we will be primarily concerned with using the printer ports. The "games" port does have potential uses though, and its possibilities will also be explored.

Advantages

So why should you bother to use the PC's joystick and printer ports for general interfacing when there is a perfectly good expansion bus? As already pointed out, there are practical difficulties in using the expansion slots, making it a rather awkward prospect for the average electronics hobbyist. The printer and joystick ports are much more straightforward, and provide no real difficulties. You simply connect your add-on to the PC via a multi-way lead terminated in the appropriate type of D connector. Even if you are equipped to make accurate double-sided printed circuit boards, the relative simplicity of interfacing to the PC's built-in interfaces could reasonably be regarded as a more attractive proposition. It is noticeable that an increasing range of ready-made PC add-ons are designed to connect to the built-in interfaces rather than the expansion bus.

Another advantage of the built-in ports is that they effectively provide you with some of the hardware for your add-ons, but at little or no cost. At little cost if you need to buy an expansion card to provide the printer of "games" port, or no cost if your computer is supplied complete with suitable ports (as most are). If you interface via the expansion slots it is necessary to include address decoding and input/output ports on the card. This means that you end up with a fair amount of circuitry before you start on the project itself! Using the built-in ports

4

means that all or most of the basic interfacing is taken care of for you.

On the face of it there is an advantage in using the expansion slots for your add-ons, as it keeps everything neat and tidy with your circuits tucked away inside the PC. In reality things are usually slightly less straightforward than this. You often seem to end up with projects that are half on the expansion card and half outside the computer, with a big lead between the two. This is because you often need to have access to the add-on. For example, EPROM programming and chip testing requires you to be able to plug chips into the add-on unit. If a project has any controls, these must be on an external unit so that you can get at them. With projects of these types, using the built-in ports would seem to be no more or less neat than using the expansion slots. It is likely to be significantly less expensive though.

Using the integral ports does have one or two drawbacks. I suppose one of these drawbacks is that it is ultimately more limiting than using the expansion slots, but this is obviously irrelevant unless you intend to do some fairly complex interfacing. For many purposes the built-in ports are perfectly adequate. Another slight drawback is that there are no power rails available on the printer ports. Only a +5 volt rail is available when using the "games" port. When using the printer ports it is possible to use the "games" port to provide a +5 volt supply, which is all that many add-ons require. When using the printer ports or "games" port it is possible to use the expansion bus as a source for all the PC's supply rails. However, this is not a particularly neat solution, and if anything beyond a simple +5 volt supply is needed, it is normal practice to provide the add-on with its own power supply unit.

Right Lines

The PC printer connector is a female 25-way D type connector. You therefore need a male 25-way D connector to make the connections to each port. When used for their intended purpose the pins of each printer port have the functions detailed in Figure 1.1. This shows the port as viewed from the outside of the computer. Looking at it another way, it shows the pin functions of the male connector as viewed from the rear. In other

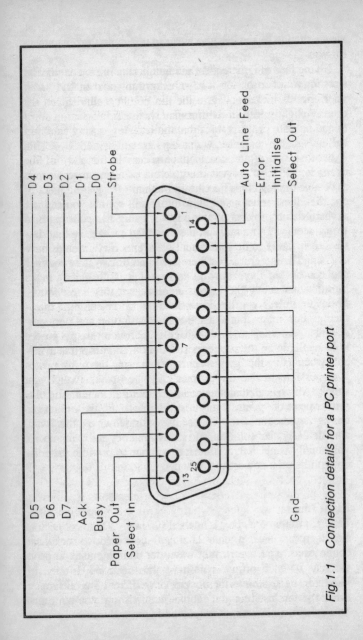

Fig.1.1 Connection details for a PC printer port

words, as viewed when you are actually making the connections to the plug.

If you are unsure about the pin numbering of practically any computer connector, it is worth bearing in mind that virtually all of these connectors have the pin numbers marked on the connectors themselves. Unfortunately, the small size of most connectors inevitably means that the lettering is very small. In the case of D type connectors matters are not helped by the fact that the numbers are moulded into the plastic body of the connectors. You may well need the aid of a magnifier to read the numbers, but this is a certain method of avoiding a set of "mirrored" connections to the D plugs.

One way of using a printer port for general interfacing is to make your add-on circuit mimic a parallel printer, so that data can be written to it in the normal way. This method does have possible advantages, since there are operating system routines and general high level support to control the flow of data to the port. If you interface to the port in the normal way, there should be no difficulty in using these routines and support. The drawback of this method is that it is very restrictive, and only permits the port to operate as a fairly basic eight bit output type.

Direct control of the printer ports permits much greater versatility, and in conjunction with some external hardware makes it possible to have numerous input and output lines. Even if you do wish to use the printer as nothing more than an eight bit output with handshaking, it might still be easier to write direct to the port, and control the flow of data using your own software routines. This type of thing is not particularly complex, and is easily integrated with the main program. I would certainly recommend direct control of the ports, and in this book we will only consider this method of interfacing.

When taking direct control of the printer ports it is best to largely forget the intended purposes of the input lines. The exception here are the eight data outputs ("D0" to "D7" in Figure 1.1). These are eight latching outputs, and it is to these that bytes of data are written when the ports are used to drive printers. Their function is normally the same when they are used for general interfacing purposes. The only difference when they are used for general interfacing is that you write data to the appropriate input/output address, and not to a DOS

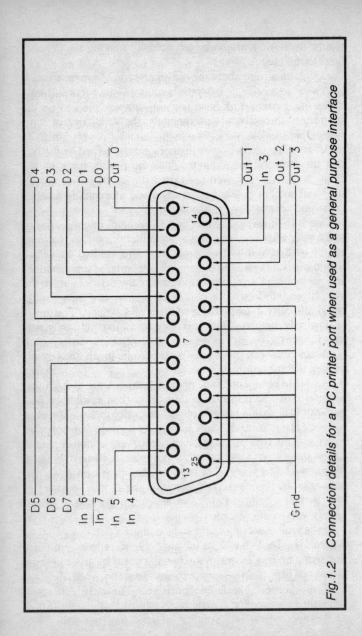

D4
D3
D2
D1
D0
$\overline{\text{Out 0}}$

$\overline{\text{Out 1}}$
In 3
Out 2
$\overline{\text{Out 3}}$

1
14

7

13 25

D5
D6
D7
In 6
$\overline{\text{In 7}}$
In 5
In 4

Gnd

Fig.1.2   Connection details for a PC printer port when used as a general purpose interface

8

device via the operating system.

With the other lines their original functions should be forgotten, and they should be thought of as input and output lines at certain addresses in the PC's input/output map. Figure 1.2 shows the pin functions with this alternative way of viewing things. As will be apparent from this diagram, in addition to the eight bit output there are four other outputs, and five input lines. Unfortunately, some of these additional inputs and outputs have built-in inverters. These are the ones which have the line marked over the pin function. This is generally a bit inconvenient, but the inverters do not place any major limitations on the ways in which the relevant lines can be used. Where the inversions are not needed they can be counteracted by using an external inverter in your interface circuit. Alternatively, the software routines can be written to take into account any unwanted inversions.

Properly Addressed

In DOS terminology the printer ports are LPT1 and LPT2. They each occupy three addresses in the PC's input/output map. Note that the 8088 series of microprocessors used in the PCs have separate memory and input/output maps, and the printer ports are obviously in the input/output map. When writing data to one of these ports, or reading from them, you must therefore use instructions that are appropriate to input/output devices. Thus, in GW BASIC you would use INP and OUT, not PEEK and POKE. The normal scheme of things is for LPT1 to be at addresses from &H378 to &H37A, and LPT2 to be at addresses from &H278 to &H27A. The decimal equivalents for these hexadecimal address ranges are 888 to 890, and 632 to 634. In this book we will deal in hexadecimal addresses, but when writing software for use with your own printer port add-ons it is obviously in order to use decimal addresses if this is your preferred way of doing things.

The table on pages 10 and 11 shows the location of each printer port input/output line in the PC's input/output map.

LPT2

&H278

Bit	Line
0	D0
1	D1
2	D2
3	D3
4	D4
5	D5
6	D6
7	D7

&H279

Bit	Line
0	unused
1	unused
2	unused
3	In 3
4	In 4
5	In 5
6	In 6
7	In 7 (inverted)

&H27A

Bit	Line
0	Out 0 (inverted)
1	Out 1 (inverted)
2	Out 2
3	Out 3 (inverted)
4	unused
5	unused
6	unused
7	unused

LPT1

&H378

Bit	Line
0	D0
1	D1
2	D2
3	D3
4	D4
5	D5
6	D6
7	D7

&H379

Bit	Line
0	unused
1	unused
2	unused
3	In 3
4	In 4
5	In 5
6	In 6
7	In 7 (inverted)

&H37A

Bit	Line
0	Out 0 (inverted)
1	Out 1 (inverted)
2	Out 2
3	Out 3 (inverted)
4	unused
5	unused
6	unused
7	unused

Writing to the eight data lines of either port is very straight-forward, and is just a matter of writing the correct value to the appropriate address. For example, to set all eight data lines of LPT2 high a value of 255 would be written to address &H278. In GW BASIC or Q BASIC this would be achieved using the OUT instruction (i.e. OUT &H278,255). There is no need to include data latches in your add-on circuits, because the data outputs are latching types.

Presumably due to the fact that some commercial peripherals for PCs use the printer port for bidirectional parallel interfacing, some people seem to have gained the impression that the data lines can be used as inputs or outputs. Unfortunately, this is not possible using a standard PC printer port. The hardware that provides the eight data lines can only provide outputs, and none of these lines can be used as inputs. Parallel data can only be input via the printer port using the slightly circuitous methods that will be described shortly, or using special non-standard printer ports.

Like the data outputs, the four handshake outputs at addresses &H27A and &H37A are latching types, and they can only act as outputs. Again, it is just a matter of writing the appropriate value to the port address. With handshake lines it would usually be easier if they could be operated entirely independently. This is clearly not possible here, because all four handshake outputs of each printer port are at the same address. Therefore, when altering the state of one output, great care must be taken not to alter the states of the other three outputs.

A standard way of achieving this is to read from the port to determine the states of the outputs, and then work out a modified value to write back to the port, so that only the desired change is made. This is not a reliable method in this case, since this is a write-only address. You can not be sure that the values read back will accurately reflect the states of the outputs. In fact it is highly unlikely that they would, and with most printer port cards a value of 255 will always be returned from the handshake output address. This is simply because no hardware is actually activated by a read operation to the handshake output addresses, and the data lines of the microprocessor are left free to drift. They all drift to the high state, giving a returned value of 255. Where necessary, your software routines must therefore be carefully written so that the program "remembers" the last value written to the handshake outputs.

Of course, with only four of the bits at each of these addresses actually used, only data values from 0 to 15 are valid. Values from 16 to 255 will not cause a software error, but only the least significant four bits of these values will affect the states of the handshake outputs. For instance, a value of 16 would set all four outputs low, and a value of 255 would set them all high. On the other hand, it would not be good programming practice to write out-of-range values to a port.

Quart Into a Pint Pot
On the face of it, the handshake inputs are only suitable for their intended purpose, since five inputs is not enough to read in bytes of data. In reality they can be used to read in bytes of data, but this requires a small amount of additional hardware, plus one of the handshake outputs. It is just a matter of using some basic multiplexing, and Figure 1.3 shows the basic setup used. Four of the handshake inputs are fed from two sets of four bit tristate buffers. The handshake output directly drives the enable input of one quad tristate buffer, but drives the enable input of the other via an inverter. Only one or other of the quad buffers will be active at any one time, and the required buffer can be selected by setting the handshake output to the appropriate state.

The lower nibble of the eight bit input is applied to one buffer, and the upper nibble is applied to the other buffer. In order to read in a complete byte it is necessary to read the two nibbles separately, and then use a simple software routine to combine the two readings in such a way that the correct value for the full byte is obtained. This method is obviously not as quick and direct as reading data in complete bytes, but even with a fairly slow PC it would probably be possible to read in a few hundred thousand bytes per second. It is certainly faster than using the serial ports, which enable data to be read at no more than a few kilobytes per second.

There is a potential problem though, and this is that the byte of data being read might change in the period between the first and second nibbles being read. This is a problem that exists with any input method that provides something less than instant

13

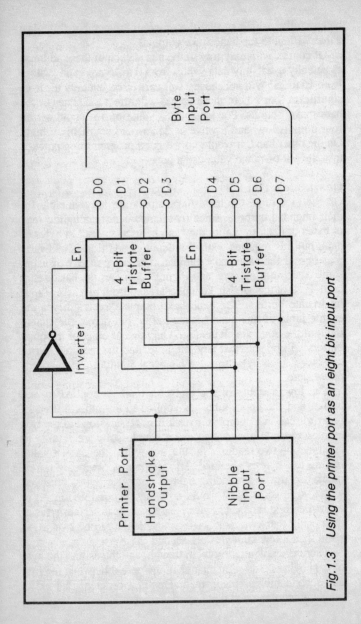

Fig. 1.3   Using the printer port as an eight bit input port

14

reading of a port. Where necessary, the problem must be dealt with using conventional handshake methods. For example, a handshake output could be used to latch input bytes into a data latch. The input port would then be used to read the bytes of data "frozen" in the data latch, rather than reading the bytes of data directly. Of course, in many cases the input data will change too slowly to create a major problem. However, even where the data changes relatively slowly it might be as well to use a software routine to check for inaccurate readings. For example, readings can be taken until three consecutive values are the same. This does not absolutely guarantee glitch-free results, but in practice would probably be sufficient to prevent any spurious readings.

Options

There is more than one way of interfacing this type of input port to the PC. Perhaps the obvious way is to drive the four most significant handshake lines from the quad buffers. The basic port reading process would then follow along these general lines. First the handshake output would be used to select the least significant nibble, and the port would be read. The returned value would then be placed into a variable. Next the handshake output would be used to select the most significant nibble, and a reading would be taken. This reading would then be stored in a second variable.

The value returned from the most significant nibble is correct, and needs no mathematical manipulation. The same is not true of the least significant nibble, which has been read in on the four most significant input lines. In order to make a correction for this it is merely necessary to divide the stored value by sixteen. Adding this value to the one read from the most significant nibble then gives the full value for the byte. In practice there is a slight problem with this method in that bit 7 is inverted. This is not a major problem as it can be corrected by using an inverter ahead of this input. Alternatively, further software could be used to invert this bit.

It is possible to avoid the problem of the inversion on bit seven by using bits three to six instead of bits four to seven. There are no internal inverters on bits three to six. The port

15

reading process is much the same as before, with the most and least significant nibbles being read, and the returned values being placed into variables. The mathematical manipulation is obviously a bit different. This time the most significant nibble does require some correction, and this is achieved by simply multiplying it by two. The least significant nibble is corrected by a division by eight. Then, as before, the two values are added together to give the value for the complete byte.

It does not matter which of the four handshake outputs is used to control the quad tristate buffers. If there are two unused handshake outputs it is possible to dispense with the inverter. Instead, each buffer is controlled from a separate handshake output, and the software controls these in such a way that only one or other of the buffers is ever active at any one time. Of course, with this method a programming error could result in both buffers being active simultaneously, and some careful programming would be needed in order to avoid this. There is also a potential problem with both buffers being activated at switch-on, prior to your controlling software being run. This might not have disastrous results, but my preferred method is to include the inverter and use a single handshake output.

Using the method of interfacing outlined here it is possible for each printer port to provide an eight bit latching output port, an eight bit input port, plus two or three handshake outputs, and one handshake input. This is sufficient for many purposes, but it is actually possible to have further expansion per port if desired. In the same way that eight input lines can be multiplexed into four input lines, 16 input lines can be multiplexed into those eight lines. This is just a matter of using two eight bit tristate buffers to provide the additional multiplexing, plus one of the spare handshake outputs to control the buffers.

Things could be taken a stage further, but multiplexing beyond 16 input lines produces a relatively complex circuit, and requires some convoluted programming in order to read the ports. My advice would be to use a proper parallel interface expansion card if large numbers of inputs are required. This is likely to be a more expensive way of tackling things, but it would also be a very much more straightforward and convenient solution to the problem.

Multiplexing techniques can also be applied to the eight data outputs, enabling two or more eight bit output ports to be provided. Again, trying to provide numerous ports in this way is probably not very practical, and a proper parallel expansion card would then be a better option. Providing two or three ports in this way is reasonably straightforward though.

Input Port

Having looked at the basic principles behind interfacing to the printer port we will now consider some practical circuits for input ports, and multiple input and output ports. We will start with basic eight bit input ports. There are numerous ways of providing the required multiplexing, and we will consider a range of alternatives here. The best method is largely dependent on the way in which the port will be used. In most cases it will not matter which method is used, and it is then just a matter of selecting the one that you find the most convenient.

The circuit of Figure 1.4 is for an input port which drives handshake inputs from D3 to D6. This is the method I generally prefer, since it avoids the complication of the inversion on bit 7. There are various tristate buffers that can be used in this application, and in this circuit a 74LS244 octal tristate buffer is used. Although this chip is normally described as an octal buffer, it is in fact two four-bit types having separate enable inputs. This makes it ideal for use in the present application.

IC2 provides an inversion so that the two halves of IC1 are driven in anti-phase. Any of the four handshake outputs could be used to control the buffers, but to keep things as straightforward as possible, in these examples the strobe output (bit 0 at pin 1 of the port) is always used. The least significant nibble is read when pin 1 is low – the most significant nibble is read when pin 1 is high. However, bear in mind that there is a built-in inversion on the strobe output, so this output is set high and low using values of 0 and 1 respectively. This simple GW BASIC routine will read the port and print the returned value on the screen. This is for an interface on LPT1, but with the appropriate addresses it will also work with an interface on LPT2. The program should work using any BASIC that is compatible with GW BASIC, including Q BASIC.

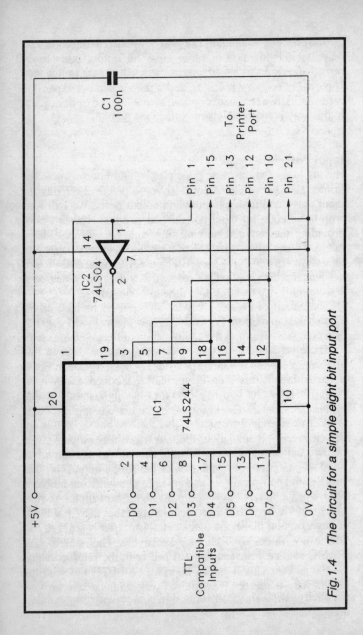

Fig. 1.4   The circuit for a simple eight bit input port

18

```
5    REM PROG TO READ IN BYTE ON BITS 3 TO 6
10   OUT &H37A,1
20   LSN = INP(&H379) AND 120
30   LSN = LSN/8
40   OUT &H37A,0
50   MSN = INP(&H379) AND 120
60   MSN = MSN * 2
70   BYTE = LSN + MSN
80   PRINT BYTE
```

Line 10 sets the control output low so that the least significant nibble is selected. This nibble is then read at line 20 and placed in the variable called "LSN". The value read from the port is bitwise ANDed with a value of 120 so that only bits three to six are read, and the other four bits are masked. The bitwise ANDing process is described in detail at the end of this chapter. Those who are unfamiliar with this procedure would be well advised to study the relevant section of this book, since it is difficult to undertake anything more than some very basic computer interfacing without a proper understanding of bitwise ANDing.

The value held in LSN is incorrect, as it has been read by the wrong lines (i.e. bits three to six instead of zero to three). When working in assembly language this type of thing can be handled using rotate or shift instructions to move the bits into the correct positions. When using a high level language it is easier to use multiplication or division to correct the positioning of bits. In this case a division by eight at line 30 produces the correct value for the least significant nibble.

At line 40 the control output is set high so that the most significant nibble is selected. This nibble is then read at line 50, and the returned value is placed in a variable called "MSN". The value of this nibble is corrected at line 60 where it is multiplied by two. Finally, the values of the two nibbles are added together to produce the full eight bit value, which is placed in the variable called "BYTE", and printed on the screen.

Although this single-chip solution to the tristate buffering looks very neat on paper, in reality it is something less than simplicity itself. The problem is simply that the pinout configuration of the 74LS244 is not as convenient as it might be. This

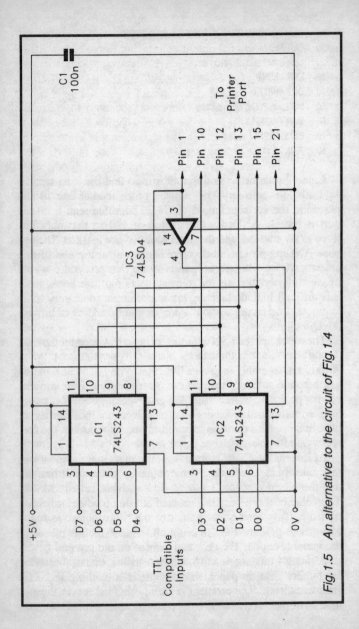

Fig.1.5   An alternative to the circuit of Fig.1.4

20

is not a major problem if you have the necessary facilities to produce intricate printed circuit boards, but it makes life difficult if you are only able to produce relatively simple boards, or you wish to use a proprietary printed circuit board such as stripboard.

For construction using stripboard, etc., the alternative circuit of Figure 1.5 should prove to be a better choice. This is based on two 74LS243 quad transceivers, but in this circuit both devices are connected to act as quad tristate buffers. The 74LS243 conveniently has all the inputs in one row of pins, and all the outputs in the other row. This makes it much easier to design a suitable component layout, particularly when using stripboard and other proprietary printed circuit boards.

The control input at pin 1 of each device is connected to the +5 volt rail, and the other control input at pin 13 of each chip then gives standard tristate control (high to enable the outputs, or low to disable them). As before, an inverter (IC2) is used to provide the required anti-phase control of the tristate buffers. Like the circuit of Figure 1.4, the control input must be low to read the least significant nibble, and high to read the most significant nibble. Therefore, the GW BASIC routine provided previously will also work with this version of the input port.

Dual Control

It is possible to do away with the inverter stage if the tristate buffers are controlled by separate handshake outputs. Obviously this will not always be feasible, since the other three handshake outputs may be required for other purposes. On the other hand, where a spare output is available, it would seem to make sense to use it in place of the inverter stage. However, bear in mind the warning given previously about both buffers being activated at switch-on. It would be advisable to check the states of the relevant handshake lines during and immediately after the computer's start-up routine. Do not use two outputs that are normally low.

Figure 1.6 shows the circuit for an eight bit input port based on a 74LS244 that uses separate handshake outputs to control the buffers. The equivalent circuit using a pair of 74LS243 quad transceivers appears in Figure 1.7. In both cases the tristate buffers are controlled by the strobe and linefeed outputs,

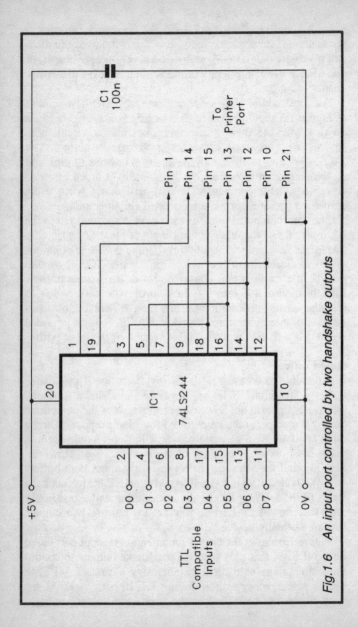

Fig.1.6 An input port controlled by two handshake outputs

22

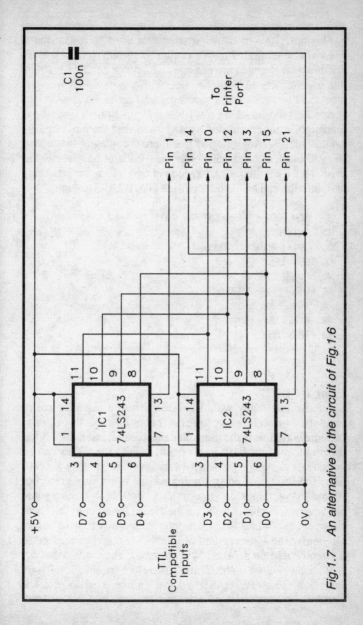

Fig.1.7   An alternative to the circuit of Fig.1.6

23

which are at bits zero and one of the handshake output port.

Obviously this modified arrangement must be read using a somewhat modified software routine. The only program lines that must be changed are the ones which use an OUT instruction to select the nibble to be read. With this modified arrangement the two handshake outputs must be set to the appropriate states. This means taking pin 1 low and pin 14 high to read the least significant nibble, and vice versa to read the most significant nibble. Bearing in mind that there are integral inversions on both of these handshake outputs, a value of one selects the least significant nibble, and a value of two selects the most significant nibble. This is the modified GW BASIC routine.

```
5    REM MODIFIED PROG TO READ IN BYTE ON BITS 3 TO 6
10   OUT &H37A,1
20   LSN = INP(&H379) AND 120
30   LSN = LSN/8
40   OUT &H37A,2
50   MSN = INP(&H379) AND 120
60   MSN = MSN * 2
70   BYTE = LSN + MSN
80   PRINT BYTE
```

Using D4 To D7

I suppose that many would consider it to be more logical to input the data on bits four to seven, rather than bits three to six. In some ways this is the more elegant solution, but it does bring the problem of the built-in inversion on bit seven. This can be counteracted using either a hardware inverter or a software routine. The additional programming needed is not very great, but it could slow things down to an unacceptable degree in some applications. Figure 1.8 shows the circuit for an eight bit input based on two74LS243s which interface to bits four to seven. Obviously the same method of interfacing could be applied to a circuit based on a 74LS244 if preferred. The circuit does not include an inverter on bit 7, and it therefore requires a software inversion. This GW BASIC routine can be used to read the port.

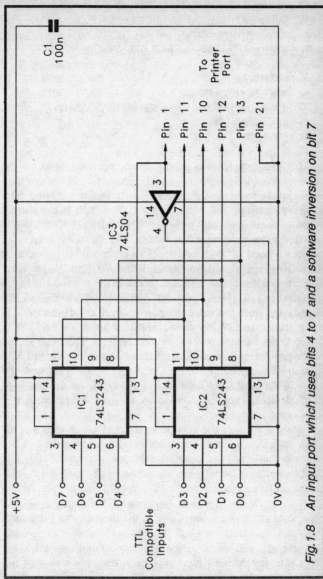

Fig. 1.8 An input port which uses bits 4 to 7 and a software inversion on bit 7

25

```
5    REM PROG TO READ IN BYTE ON BITS 4 TO 7 (SOFTWARE INVERSION)
10   OUT &H37A,1
20   LSN = INP(&H379) AND 240
30   IF LSN > 127 THEN LSN = LSN–128 ELSE LSN = LSN+128
40   LSN = LSN/16
50   OUT &H37A,0
60   MSN = INP(&H379) AND 240
70   IF MSN > 127 THEN MSN = MSN–128 ELSE MSN = MSN+128
80   BYTE = MSN + LSN
90   PRINT BYTE
```

This program follows along much the same lines as the
routines provided previously, but the processing of the raw data
is obviously somewhat different. Firstly, at lines 20 and 60 a
masking value of 240 is used (not 120), which is the correct
value to mask bits four to seven. The most significant bit is
inverted when reading either nibble, and the same correction
process is used for both nibbles. This correction is provided at
lines 30 (least significant nibble) and 70 (most significant
nibble). First a check is made to see if the returned value is
greater than 127. If it is, the most significant bit is high, and 128
is deducted from the value in order to set it low. If the value is
not greater than 127, the most significant bit is low, and 128 is
added to the value in order to set this bit high. This second part
of the processing is provided, where necessary, by the "ELSE"
section of the program lines. Once doctored in this way the
value in the most significant nibble is correct, but the least significant nibble must be divided by 16 (line 40) to produce a
fully corrected value.

Figure 1.9 shows the version of the port which uses a hardware inversion on bit 7. The inversion is provided by IC3b,
which is one of the five otherwise unused inverters of IC3. The
double inversion on bit 7 clearly introduces a small delay relative to the other bits. In practice this delay is likely to be far too
short to be of any practical importance. It is not possible to
input data at super-fast rates due to the limitations of the computer, and also because the data is read as two separate nibbles.
Reading this version of the port is very straightforward, since
there is no inversion on bit 7 to contend with, and no correction
is needed to the value read from the most significant nibble.

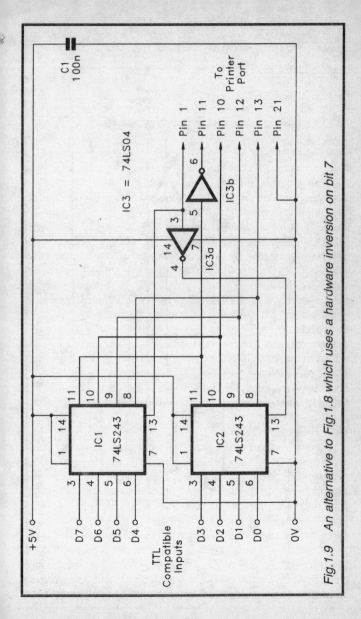

Fig. 1.9   An alternative to Fig. 1.8 which uses a hardware inversion on bit 7

27

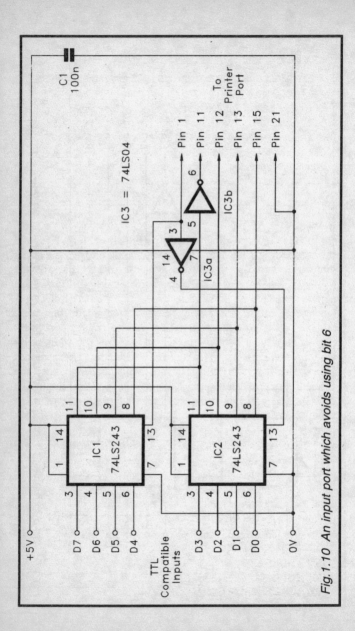

Fig.1.10 An input port which avoids using bit 6

28

This simple GW BASIC routine will read the port and print the returned value on the screen.

```
5    REM PROG TO READ BYTE ON BITS 4 TO 7 (HARDWARE INVERSION)
10   OUT &H37A,1
20   LSN = INP(&H379) AND 240
30   LSN = LSN/16
40   OUT &H37A,0
50   MSN = INP(&H379) AND 240
60   BYTE = MSN + LSN
70   PRINT BYTE
```

BITS 3, 4, 5, AND 7

On the face of it, reading in bytes on bits three, four, five, and seven is doing things the hard way. Apparently some users prefer this approach because it avoids using bit six, and the possibility of generating interrupts by activating this line. I can not say that I have ever experienced any problems of this type, but we will consider this method of interfacing for those who prefer to take the conservative approach to printer port interfacing. Figure 1.10 shows the circuit diagram for an eight bit input port which uses this method of interfacing. This provides a hardware inversion on bit seven, which helps to keep the amount of mathematical processing of data to a minimum. This GW BASIC program reads the port and prints the returned value on the screen.

```
10   REM PROG TO READ BYTE ON BITS 3, 4, 5, AND 7 (HARDWARE
     INVERSION)
20   OUT &H37A,1
30   LSN = INP(&H379) AND 184
40   D7 = LSN AND 128
50   D3TOD5 = LSN AND 56
60   D7 = D7/16
70   D3TOD5 = D3TOD5/8
80   LSN = D3TOD5 +  D7
90   OUT &H37A,0
100  MSN = INP(&H379) AND 184
110  D7 = MSN AND 128
```

```
120   D3TOD5 = MSN AND 56
130   D3TOD5 = D3TOD5 * 2
140   MSN = D3TOD5 + D7
150   BYTE = MSN + LSN
160   PRINT BYTE
```

Line 20 selects the least significant nibble, and then line 30 reads it in and masks off the unwanted bits. The next line takes the value from bit seven and places it in variable "D7", again using bitwise ANDing to mask off the unwanted bits. The same process is then used to read bits three, four, and five, and place the appropriate value in the variable called "D3TOD5". Lines 60 and 70 correct the values in the two variables using division rates of 16 ("D7") and eight ("D3TOD5"). The values in these variables are then added together to give the correct value for the least significant nibble (variable "LSN").

At line 90 the most significant nibble is selected, and the same basic procedure is used to read in this nibble and produce a corrected value for it. However, no multiplication or division is needed to correct the value read on bit seven, and multiplication by two is needed in order to correct bits three to five. Adding variables "LSN" and "MSN" then provides the full and correct value for the byte of data, which is then printed on the screen.

The circuit of Figure 1.11 interfaces to bits three to five plus bit seven, but it does not provide a hardware inversion. This port can be used with this GW BASIC program.

```
10    REM PROG TO READ BYTE ON BITS 3, 4, 5, AND 7 (HARDWARE
      INVERSION)
20    OUT &H37A,1
30    LSN = INP(&H379) AND 184
40    D7 = LSN AND 128
50    IF D7 > 127 THEN D7 = 0 ELSE D7 = 128
60    D3TOD5 = LSN AND 56
70    D7 = D7/16
80    D3TOD5 = D3TOD5/8
90    LSN = D3TOD5 + D7
100   OUT &H37A,0
110   MSN = INP(&H379) AND 184
```

```
120  D7 = MSN AND 128
130  IF D7 > 127 THEN D7 = 0 ELSE D7 = 128
140  D3TOD5 = MSN AND 56
150  D3TOD5 = D3TOD5 * 2
160  MSN = D3TOD5 + D7
170  BYTE = MSN + LSN
180  PRINT BYTE
```

This is basically the same as the previous program, but lines 50 and 130 are used to provide the software inversions on bit 7. Whether this method of interfacing is used with software or hardware inversions, it is clearly a rather convoluted way of tackling things. Consequently, I would not recommend using this method as a standard means of interfacing to a PC printer port. It is certainly a method that I would only adopt if the more simple methods should prove to be problematic.

Dual Inputs
It is not difficult to use the printer port's handshake lines to provide two eight bit input ports, and it is just a matter of using additional multiplexing controlled by one of the spare handshake outputs. Figure 1.12 shows one way of providing the additional multiplexing. Note that this circuit requires an eight bit input port, and that it must therefore be added onto one of the input ports described previously. It can not be used straight onto the printer port because the unaided printer port has an insufficient number of inputs.

The circuit is based on two 74LS541 8 bit tristate buffers. Their inputs act as the two eight bit input ports, and their outputs drive the basic eight bit input port. IC3 is controlled direct from "Out 2" of the printer port (the "Initialise" handshake output), but IC2 is controlled via an inverter. If the basic input port uses one or two inverters, IC1 can be an unused section of the 74LS04 used in the basic input port circuit. The inversion provided by IC1 provides the required anti-phase operation of the buffers, with IC2 enabled when "Out 2" is high, and IC3 enabled when "Out 2" is low.

The 74LS541 actually has a two input AND gate ahead of its active low enable input. The inputs of the gate are accessible at pins 1 and 19. The gating is not required in this case, so pin 19

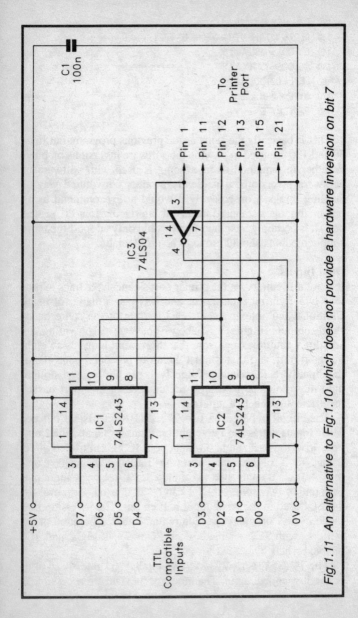

Fig.1.11 An alternative to Fig.1.10 which does not provide a hardware inversion on bit 7

32

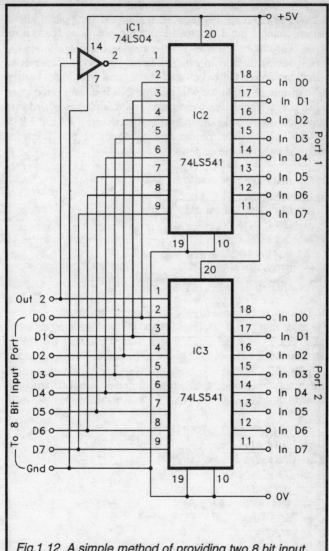

Fig.1.12 A simple method of providing two 8 bit input ports

33

is connected to the 0 volt rail, and pin 1 is used as a straight-forward negative enable input. If it suits the component layout better, connect pin 1 to ground and use pin 19 as the control input. The circuit provides exactly the same action either way.

Obviously the way in which the dual port is read depends on which version of the basic input port circuit is utilized. For the sake of this example we will assume that it is connected to an input port which drives bits four to seven, and uses a hardware inversion on bit 7. In other words, the circuit of Figure 1.9 or an equivalent. This routine will read port 1 and print the returned value on the screen.

```
5    REM PROG TO READ PORT 1
10   OUT &H37A,5
20   LSN = INP(&H379) AND 240
30   LSN = LSN/16
40   OUT &H37A,4
50   MSN = INP(&H379) AND 240
60   BYTE = MSN + LSN
70   PRINT BYTE
```

This operates in exactly the same way as the program to read the basic input port, but lines 10 and 40 have been modified to take "Out 2" high, so that IC2 is activated and port 1 is select-ed. Remember that "Out 2", unlike the other three handshake outputs, does not have a built-in inversion. It is therefore set high using a value of 4, and low using a value of 0. This ver-sion of the program sets "Out 2" low so that port 2 is read.

```
5    REM PROG TO READ PORT 2
10   OUT &H37A,1
20   LSN = INP(&H379) AND 240
30   LSN = LSN/16
40   OUT &H37A,0
50   MSN = INP(&H379) AND 240
60   BYTE = MSN + LSN
70   PRINT BYTE
```

Figure 1.13 shows the circuit for an alternative dual input circuit. This is based two 74LS245 octal transceivers, which

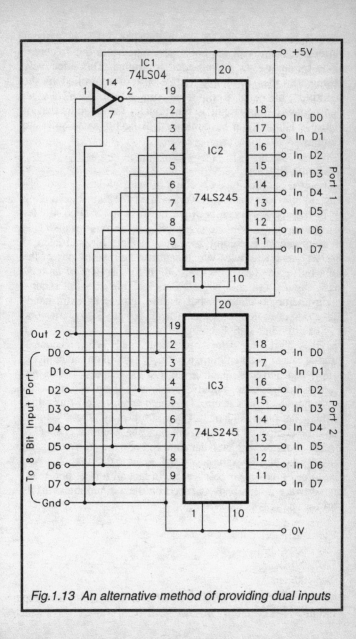

Fig.1.13 An alternative method of providing dual inputs

seem to be a bit easier to obtain than the 74LS541 tristate-buffers. IC1 and IC2 are both hard wired into the "receive" mode by having pin 1 connected to ground. This effectively downgrades them to simple tristate buffers, controlled via the negative chip enable input at pin 19 of each device. Consequently, this circuit is functionally the same as that of Figure 1.12, and can be controlled using the same software routines.

Grabbing Bytes

As pointed out previously, reading in bytes of data as two separate nibbles can cause problems when the data is changing fairly rapidly. A change between the first and second nibbles being read could produce completely erroneous results. This problem can be overcome by using an eight bit data latch to "freeze" complete bytes which can then be read by one of the eight bit input ports. This is the digital equivalent of an analogue sample-and-hold circuit. Data latching does not require much additional circuitry, but it does require an extra hand-shake output to control the data latch. Figure 1.14 shows one way of providing data latching.

IC1 is a 74LS373 octal "transparent" latch. When its control input at pin 11 is taken high, the binary pattern on the inputs is simply transferred straight through to the outputs. Taking pin 11 low "freezes" the outputs, and latches them with the data present on the inputs as pin 11 made the high-to-low transition. In this example pin 11 of IC1 is controlled by "Out 2", but it could be controlled by any spare handshake output. This GW BASIC program will latch data into IC1 and then read it. Again, for the sake of this example we will assume that the input port circuit of Figure 1.9 is being used. In fact all further port reading software in this book is based on the assumption that this port (or an equivalent) is used.

```
10   REM PROG TO READ BYTE VIA DATA LATCH (74LS373)
20   OUT &H37A,0
30   OUT &H37A,4
40   OUT &H37A,0
45   FOR DELAY = 1 TO 30000:NEXT DELAY
50   OUT &H37A,1
```

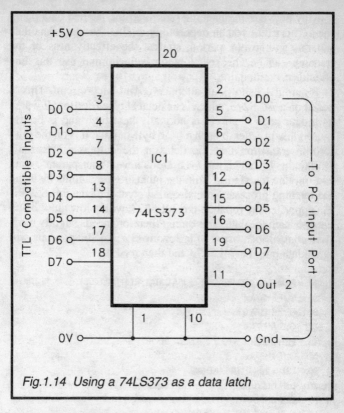

```
+5V o
                        20

         3                         2
DO o                              o DO
         4                         5
D1 o                              o D1
         7                         6
D2 o                              o D2
         8                         9
D3 o            IC1               o D3
        13                        12
D4 o                              o D4
        14         74LS373        15
D5 o                              o D5
        17                        16
D6 o                              o D6
        18                        19
D7 o                              o D7

                                  11
                                  o Out 2

          1        10
0V o                              o Gnd
```

Fig.1.14 Using a 74LS373 as a data latch

```
60    LSN = INP(&H379) AND 240
70    LSN = LSN/16
80    OUT &H37A,0
90    MSN = INP(&H379) AND 240
100   BYTE = MSN + LSN
110   PRINT BYTE
```

This is just the normal port reading routine, but with lines 20 to 40 added to provide a positive latching pulse prior to the port being read. It is at line 40, where "Out 2" goes through a high-to-low transition, that the data is latched into the 74LS373. Line 45 is not part of the reading routine, and it simply provides a delay between the latching pulse and the latched data being read. This gives you an opportunity to alter the input data during this in-between period, so that the effectiveness of the latching can be checked. Obviously in normal use this line should be omitted.

Figure 1.15 shows an alternative data latch circuit. This is based on a 74LS273, which is an octal D type flip/flop. It works as a data latch if pin 11 is normally held high and is briefly pulsed low in order to latch a fresh byte of data. It is on the low-to-high transition that the data on the outputs is "frozen". Unlike the 74LS373, the 74LS273 is never "transparent". Data can only be transferred from the inputs to the outputs by using the latching process. Note also, that control of the 74LS273 is the opposite way round to the 74LS373, with a low pulse being used to latch the data. This circuit therefore needs slightly modified control software. The following GW BASIC program will latch data into the 74LS273 and then read it.

```
10   REM PROG TO READ BYTE VIA DATA LATCH (74LS273)
20   OUT &H37A,4
30   OUT &H37A,0
40   OUT &H37A,4
45   FOR DELAY = 1 TO 25000:NEXT DELAY
50   OUT &H37A,5
60   LSN = INP(&H379) AND 240
70   LSN = LSN/16
80   OUT &H37A,4
90   MSN = INP(&H379) AND 240
100  BYTE = MSN + LSN
110  PRINT BYTE
```

Dual Outputs

The eight data outputs of the printer port (D0 to D5 in Figures 1.1 and 1.2) provide a ready-made eight bit output port. This makes writing bytes of data much easier than reading them, since it is possible to write complete bytes. Simply write the appropriate value to input/output address &H378 (LPT1) or &H278 (LPT2) and the data lines will take up the correct binary pattern. There are no inversions on any of these lines, and they are all TTL compatible.

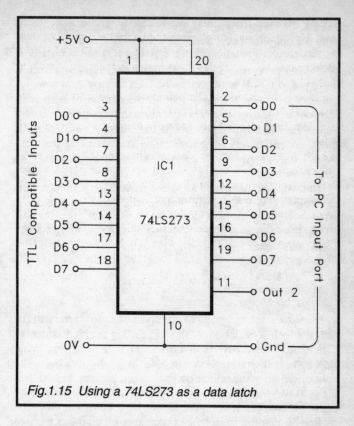

Fig.1.15 Using a 74LS273 as a data latch

Using the single eight bit output to provide two eight bit outputs is very simple, and it requires nothing more than a couple of data latches, with each one controlled from a separate handshake output. Figure 1.16 shows one way of providing an extra output port. This uses two 74LS273 octal D type flip/flops as the data latches. The handshake control lines are normally held in the high state. In order to write a byte of data to port 1 the data is first written to the data lines of the printer port. The handshake line used to control IC1 ("Out 2" in this example) is then taken low and high again. On the low-to-high transition the new byte of data is latched onto IC1's outputs. Data is written to port 2 in much the same way, but it is handshake line

39

"Out 3" that is pulsed low in order to latch the new byte of data onto the outputs of port 2.

The negative reset inputs of IC1 and IC2 are simply connected to the positive supply rail so that they have no effect. If preferred, a C – R network can be used to provide a negative pulse at switch-on to ensure that all the outputs of both ports start out in the low state. This is only necessary where random values on the port outputs could have dire consequences. It might require a very long reset pulse to ensure that the computer's start-up and initial testing routines do not override the reset pulse.

The software to write data to the ports is very simple. This example in GW BASIC will write a value of 123 to port 1.

```
10   REM PROG TO WRITE A BYTE OF DATA TO PORT 1 (74LS273 LATCHES)
20   OUT &H37A,4
30   OUT &H378,123
40   OUT &H37A,0
50   OUT &H37A,4
```

Line 20 sets the handshake outputs at their correct initial states, which is with both of them in the high state. Remember that "Out 3" has a built-in inversion, and a value of zero rather than eight is therefore needed in order to set this line high. The data is written to the printer port's data lines at line 30, and then the next two lines produce a low pulse on "Out 2", while leaving "Out 3" high. It is on the low-to-high transition produced by line 50 that the fresh byte of data appears on the outputs of port 1.

Writing data to port 2 uses a similar process. This example GW BASIC routine writes a value of 231 to port 2.

```
10   REM PROG TO WRITE A BYTE OF DATA TO PORT 2 (74LS273 LATCHES)
20   OUT &H37A,4
30   OUT &H378,231
40   OUT &H37A,12
50   OUT &H37A,4
```

Again, line 20 sets the correct initial states on the handshake outputs, and the value for port 2 is written to the printer port

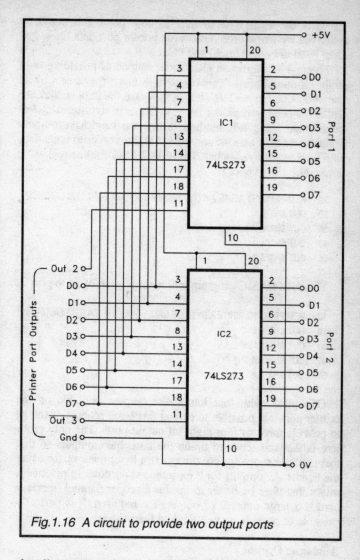

Fig.1.16 A circuit to provide two output ports

data lines at line 30. Lines 40 and 50 then provide a negative pulse on "Out 3", but leave "Out 2" high so that the data on the port 1 outputs is left unchanged. Of course, if it was necessary

41

to write the same byte of data to both ports, this could be achieved by writing the data to the printer port data lines, and then pulsing both "Out 2" and "Out 3".

Figure 1.17 shows an alternative method of providing twin eight bit output ports. This operates in much the same way as the circuit of Figure 1.15, but in this case the data latches are 74LS373 octal transparent latches. The only significant difference when using this method is that the handshake outputs should normally be low, and pulsed high in order to latch data into their respective latches. This GW BASIC routine will write a value of 156 to port 1.

```
10    REM PROG TO WRITE A BYTE OF DATA TO PORT 1 (74LS373 LATCHES)
20    OUT &H37A,8
30    OUT &H378,156
40    OUT &H37A,0
50    OUT &H37A,8
```

This GW BASIC program will write a value of 54 to port 2.

```
10    REM PROG TO WRITE A BYTE OF DATA TO PORT 2 (74LS373 LATCHES)
20    OUT &H37A,8
30    OUT &H378,156
40    OUT &H37A,4
50    OUT &H37A,8
```

Of course, with four handshake outputs available on the printer port it is possible to extend this basic scheme of things to provide three or four eight bit output ports. The only problem is that this tends to tie-up the handshake outputs so that there is little scope for providing extra input lines, or for using the handshake outputs for their intended purpose. In practice it might therefore be better to opt for a proper parallel interface card if a large number of outputs are required. It is perfectly possible to provide up to 32 output lines though.

Analogue Output
An eight bit digital to analogue converter is easily interfaced to the eight data outputs of the printer port, and matters are simplified by the fact that these lines are latching types. The

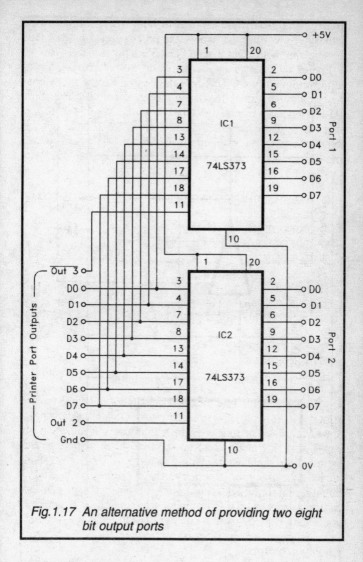

Fig.1.17 An alternative method of providing two eight
bit output ports

Ferranti ZN426E is a good choice for most applications that
require a straightforward digital to analogue converter. Figure
1.18 shows the circuit diagram for converter based on this chip.

43

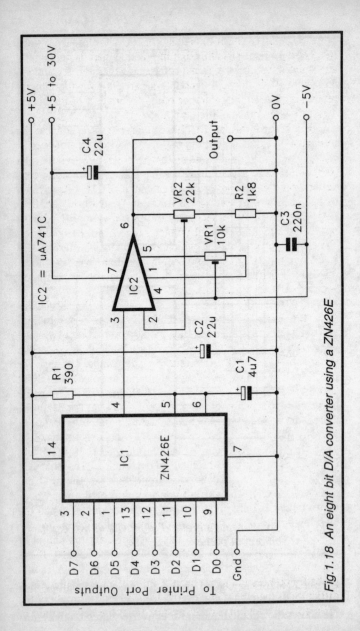

Fig. 1.18 An eight bit D/A converter using a ZN426E

44

The ZN426E has a built-in precision 2.55 volt reference source. It is not essential to use this, but in practice there is not usually any point in using an external reference generator. R1 and C1 are the load resistor and decoupling capacitor for the integral reference source. The reference output at pin 6 of IC1 connects direct to the reference input at pin 5.

The output voltage at pin 4 has a full scale value equal to the reference potential. Using the internal 2.55 volt reference generator gives an output voltage that is equal to 10 millivolts (0.01 volts) per l.s.b. Writing a value of (say) 120 to the converter would therefore produce a potential of 1.2 volts at pin 4 of IC1 (120 × 0.01 volts = 1.2 volts). In "real world" applications it will usually be necessary to use some amplification to produce the required output voltage range from the converter. This is the purpose of IC2, which also provides buffering. IC2 is an operational amplifier used in the non-inverting mode. VR1 is the offset null control, and this is set for optimum accuracy at low output voltages.

VR2 is part of the negative feedback network, and it enables the closed loop voltage gain of IC2 to be varied between unity and about 13 times. This enables the maximum output voltage to be set anywhere between 2.55 volts and about 28 volts. The upper limit is set by the maximum positive supply voltage for IC2, which is 30 volts. The maximum output potential is about 2 volts less than the positive supply voltage, and this must be borne in mind when selecting the supply voltage. For example, there is no point in trying to set a maximum output potential of 12 volts if the supply voltage is only 12 volts. An output of 12 volts would require a supply potential of at least 14 volts, and a 15 volt supply would be the obvious choice. Note that IC1 and the rest of the main converter circuit must be powered from a +5 volt supply. The current consumption of the main converter circuit is only about 10 milliamps incidentally, and the output amplifier only draws two or three milliamps.

A –5 volt supply is needed in order to permit the output of IC2 to swing right down to the 0 volt supply voltage. If the circuit is powered from a mains power supply unit it will probably be possible to produce a –5 volt supply without any difficulty. If the circuit is powered from a battery supply or the PC's +5 volt supply (via the joystick port) the best method of providing the –5 volt supply might be to use a negative supply generator.

Figure 1.19 shows the circuit diagram for a simple negative supply generator based on an ICL7660 (or equivalent). This chip provides the negative supply using electronic switching. The basic action of the circuit is to first connect C2 across the input supply, and then across the output and smoothing capacitor C1. The polarity of C2 is swopped-over during the switching process so that a positive input is changed to a negative output. This method is not particularly efficient, and the loaded output voltage is likely to fall some way short of –5 volts. However, the negative supply voltage will be sufficient to permit the output of converter to reach 0 volts.

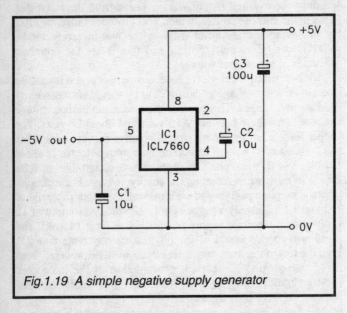

Fig.1.19 A simple negative supply generator

An alternative approach is to use a device for IC2 that permits single supply d.c. operation. Figure 1.20 shows the circuit diagram for a converter having an output amplifier of this type. This is much the same as the original circuit, but with the –5 volt supply and its decoupling capacitor omitted. Instead, the

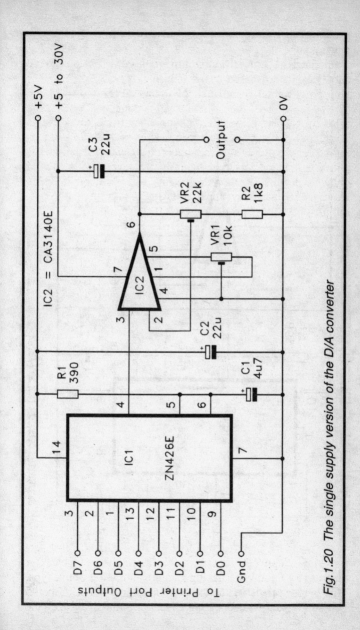

Fig.1.20 The single supply version of the D/A converter

47

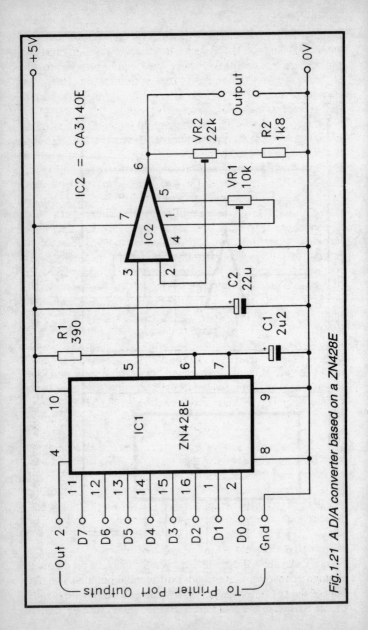

Fig.1.21 A D/A converter based on a ZN428E

48

negative supply pin and the wiper of VR1 connect to the 0 volt supply rail. The CA3140E seems to work very well in this type of circuit, and it can provide very low output voltages provided the loading on the output is kept within reason. However, this circuit is not likely to be as accurate at very low output voltages as one which uses a negative supply.

Figure 1.21 shows the circuit diagram for an eight bit digital to analogue converter that utilizes the Ferranti ZN428E. This device is very similar to the ZN426E, and it is basically just a ZN426E having an integral 8 bit data latch on the digital inputs. This circuit would be useful if it was necessary to drive two, three, or even four converters from the printer port. In this example the data latch is controlled by the printer port's "Out 2" handshake output. If "Out 2" is taken low, the data latch becomes "transparent", and the data on D0 to D7 is fed straight through to the converter circuit. The circuit then effectively operates as a converter based on a ZN426E. Taking "Out 2" high latches the data on the digital inputs into the converter.

In use the ZN428E is therefore much like a 74LS273 data latch, with the control input being held high under standby conditions. In order to latch fresh data into the converter it is pulsed low, and it is on the low-to-high transition that data is latched into the converter. In practice each converter circuit would be driven from the data outputs of the printer port, and controlled by a different handshake output. Four handshake outputs permit up to four converters to be driven from the printer port. Normally all the handshake outputs in use would be held in the high state. To write data to a converter the appropriate bit pattern is first written to the printer port's data outputs, and then the appropriate handshake output is pulsed low.

Due to the inclusion of a data latch at its input, the ZN428E has a much higher current consumption than the ZN426E. In fact it's about 20 milliamps higher. The settling time for both devices is no more than about one microsecond.

Differential Outputs

Figure 1.22 shows the circuit diagram for an eight bit digital to analogue converter that provides differential outputs. The outputs of the converter are at approximately 0 volts with a value of 128 written to the data inputs. Higher values take the normal

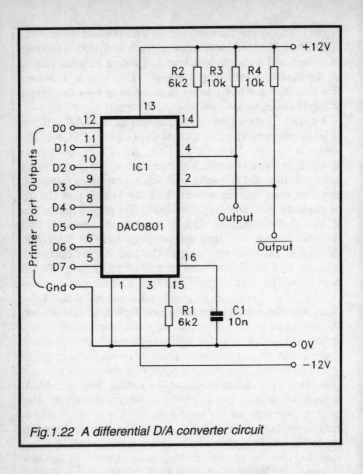

Fig.1.22 A differential D/A converter circuit

output more negative, and the not output more positive. Lower values have the opposite effect. This may seem to be round the wrong way, and it might seem more logical to have the normal output sent more positive by higher values, and the not output sent more negative by lower values. Things do not operate that way simply because the outputs are current sinks, and higher values give increased current flow at the normal output. This gives greater voltage across the load resistor, and reduced output voltage.

50

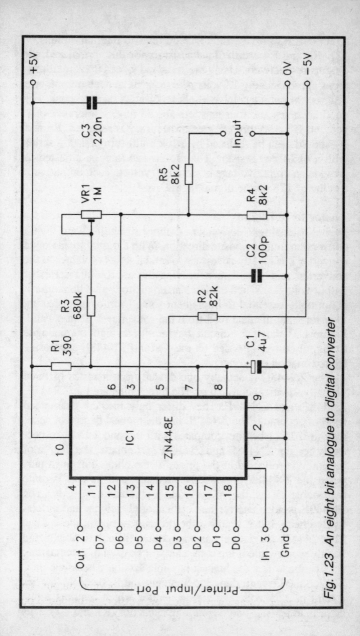

Fig. 1.23 An eight bit analogue to digital converter

51

R1 and R2 provide reference currents to internal circuits of IC1. R3 and R4 are the load resistors for the normal and not outputs respectively. Using the specified values the circuit provides approximately 12 volts peak-to-peak at each output, or a differential output voltage of about 24 volts peak-to-peak. For good accuracy the four resistors should have a tolerance of 1 percent. If a very high degree of accuracy is required, R3 and R4 should each be replaced by a 10k multi-turn preset in series with a 4k7 fixed resistor. The presets can then be adjusted to provide an output voltage of exactly 0 volts at each output with a value of 128 on the digital inputs.

Analogue To Digital
Digital to analogue conversion is more straightforward than a conversion in the opposite direction. With a digital to analogue converter it is merely necessary to send a series of values to the converter, and it will then provide the appropriate series of output voltages. When using an analogue to digital converter it is normally essential to implement some form of handshaking to ensure that the data read from the converter is always valid. Figure 1.23 shows the circuit diagram for an eight bit analogue to digital converter based on the Ferranti ZN448E successive approximation converter.

The ZN448E is actually one device from a series of three virtually identical converters. The three chips are the ZN447E, ZN448E, and ZN449E. They differ only in their guaranteed level of accuracy. The ZN447E has the highest degree of accuracy at 0.25 l.s.b. This compares with 0.5 and 1 l.s.b. respectively for the ZN448E and ZN449E. Of course, the degree of accuracy is reflected in the prices of the chips. For most purposes the ZN448E is perfectly adequate, and its cost is quite reasonable. It is the most readily obtainable version. The ZN449E is adequate for non-critical applications, and is relatively cheap, but it seems to be difficult to obtain these days. The ZN447E is relatively expensive and difficult to obtain, and is only worthwhile if the converter will be used in a demanding application where the highest possible accuracy is essential.

Like the Ferranti digital to analogue chips, the ZN448E has a built-in 2.55 volt reference generator which requires a discrete load resistor and decoupling capacitor (R1 and C1). This sets the full scale sensitivity of the chip at 2.55 volts, but for optimum accuracy an input attenuator and zero offset circuit must be used. This type of input circuit is needed in order to compensate for a slight lack of accuracy at low input voltages. To counteract this problem a small positive offset voltage must be added to the input signal. In this circuit the input attenuation is provided by R4 and R5, which effectively halves the sensitivity of the converter. The full scale input voltage of the circuit as a whole is therefore about 5.1 volts. The positive offset voltage is provided by R3 and VR1. The latter is adjusted to give optimum accuracy with small input voltages. The input circuit is basically just a passive mixer which combines the input voltage and the small positive offset voltage.

Obviously different values can be used for R4 and R5 in order to set different full scale voltages. In "real world" applications it will often be necessary to make one of the attenuator resistors a preset type so that the input sensitivity can be set at precisely the required level. The output resistance of the attenuator (i.e. the parallel resistance of R4 and R5) should always be about 4k though. Otherwise the offset circuit might not be able to provide a suitable offset potential. R3 and VR1 can be omitted if a high degree of accuracy at very low input voltages is not required.

C2 is the timing capacitor in IC1's internal clock generator circuit. The maximum clock frequency at which the ZN448E series is guaranteed to operate reliably is 1MHz, although all the devices in this series that I have tested seemed to work well at substantially higher clock rates. The specified value for C2 sets the clock frequency at a little under 1MHz, and gives a conversion time of about 10 microseconds (nine clock cycles). The value of C2 could be made lower in an attempt to produce a faster conversion time, but in the vast majority of applications there would be no point in doing this. Even as things stand, the circuit is capable of around 100,000 conversions per second, which is more than adequate for most practical applications. It is higher than is really necessary for most audio digitising for example. In order to operate the circuit at such a high rate of conversion it is necessary to use a suitably fast programming language, such as assembly language or a fast compiled language.

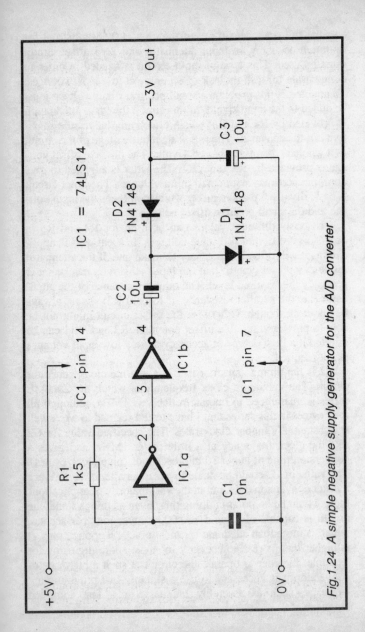

Fig.1.24 A simple negative supply generator for the A/D converter

IC1 = 74LS14

+5V

R1
1k5

IC1a

IC1b

IC1 pin 14

C1
10n

IC1 pin 7

0V

C2
10u

D1
1N4148

D2
1N4148

C3
10u

−3V Out

R2 is the "tail" resistor in the comparator stage at the input of IC1. This must be fed from a negative supply, and the specified value for R2 is correct for a –5 volt supply. Its value should be such that a current flow of about 60 microamps is produced. A value of 47k is suitable for a –3 volt supply, and a value of 180k is apposite for a –12 volt supply. Since the current consumption from the negative supply is so low it is possible to provide it via a very simple negative supply generator. Figure 1.24 shows the circuit for a low cost negative supply generator that utilizes a couple of the inverter/triggers in a 74LS14. IC1a operates as a simple relaxation oscillator, and IC1b provides buffering. Note that IC1 must be a 74LS14 and not a 74LS04 (which does not have built-in triggering, and will not oscillate in this circuit). The output voltage from this circuit is only about –3 volts, so R2 in the converter should have a value of 47k if this circuit is used to provide the negative supply.

The digital outputs of IC1 in Figure 1.23 are tristate types which are controlled via pin 2. In this example circuit pin 2 is simply connected to the negative supply rail so that the outputs are permanently enabled. The outputs are then read via one of the eight bit input ports described previously. Obviously it would be possible to use two or three analogue input ports by using the printer port's spare handshake outputs to control the tristate outputs of the converters. This would use the same basic technique that was used for the dual input ports described previously (Figures 1.12 and 1.13).

This converter does not operate on the basis of providing a continuous series of readings, with the most up-to-date reading appearing on its data outputs. A reading must be initiated by pulsing pin 4 low. The reading process commences when pin 4 returns to the high state. It is essential that the converter is not read until the conversion process has been completed. There are two ways of tackling this problem, and my preferred method is to simply use a timing loop to provide a suitable delay. Remember that the conversion time is no more than about 10 microseconds, so a hold-off of about 10 to 12 microseconds is sufficient to ensure that the converter is not read prematurely. If necessary, a suitable delaying routine can be found with the aid of some trial and error. With many programming languages, including GW BASIC, it is unlikely that the program would run fast enough to read the converter too soon, avoiding the need for any form of hold-off. It is then just a matter of initiating a conversion and then starting the reading process.

The second method of tackling the problem is to monitor the "end of conversion" output at pin 1 of IC1. In this example circuit "In 3" of the printer port is used to do this. It is assumed here that bits four to seven are used to provide the eight bit input port. Pin 1 goes low during a conversion, and a software loop can therefore be used to monitor this output and provide a hold-off until it returns to the high state. The obvious drawback to this method is that it ties up the only remaining handshake input.

As already pointed out, when reading the port using GW BASIC there is no real risk of reading the converter prematurely, even if you are using a very fast PC. This enables the converter to be read using a simple routine such as this one.

```
10    REM PROG TO READ A/D CONVERTER (VIA BITS 4 TO 7, HARDWARE
      INVERTER)
20    OUT &H37A,4
30    OUT &H37A,0
40    OUT &H37A,4
50    OUT &H37A,5
60    LSN = INP(&H379) AND 240
70    LSN = LSN/16
80    OUT &H37A,4
90    MSN = INP(&H379) AND 240
100   BYTE = MSN + LSN
110   PRINT BYTE
```

Lines 20 to 40 provide a low pulse on "Out 2" that initiates a conversion. The rest of the program is basically just the standard routine for reading the input port. The only change from the norm is that the values in lines 50 and 80 have been modified to hold "Out 2" in the high state so that a new conversion is not accidentally initiated here.

Joystick Port

Connection details for the PC "games" port are provided in Figure 1.25. The connector on the computer is a female 15 way

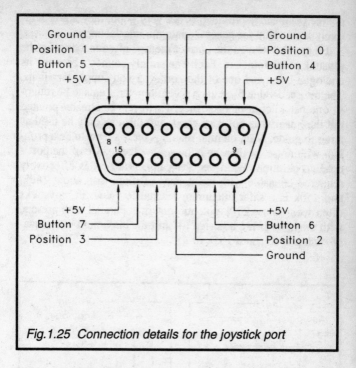

Fig.1.25 Connection details for the joystick port

D type, and you therefore need a male 15 way D connector to
make connections to this port. It is primarily intended for use
with two joysticks, which must be potentiometer style joysticks
designed for use with PCs. The "Position" inputs read the settings of the potentiometers, and two of these are needed per
joystick (one to provide the X co-ordinate, and the other to provide the Y co-ordinate). The "Button" inputs read the "fire-
buttons", and there are two of these per joystick.

When using the joystick port as a general purpose interface
it is better to think in terms of the pin identifications shown in
Figure 1.26. The inputs that read the potentiometers are a form
of analogue input, but they operate in a relatively crude fashion. As explained previously, they directly read the resistance
of the potentiometers, rather than reading their wiper voltages.
For their intended purpose the analogue inputs function well
enough, but because they read resistance not voltage, and the

degree of linearity provided is not very good, they are of relatively little value for general analogue interfacing.

Figure 1.27 shows the correct method of connection for the joystick potentiometers. Each one simply connects between its analogue input and one of the port's +5 volt supply terminals. The returned value from each potentiometer seems to be roughly one per kilohm of resistance. However, as already pointed out the linearity is not very good, and this can only be used as a rough guide. Also, on high readings there seems to be a problem with noise, or there may be some other cause of the port's erratic operation. Whatever the cause, the port is effectively rendered unusable with resistances of more than about 180k, and 150k is a safer maximum resistance value. PC joysticks often seem to use 220k potentiometers in parallel with presets, with the latter being adjusted to limit the maximum resistance of each pair to about 105k or so.

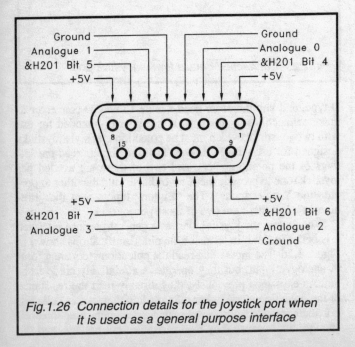

Fig.1.26 Connection details for the joystick port when it is used as a general purpose interface

The "firebutton" inputs can be read using the built-in functions of many high level languages, including GW BASIC and Q BASIC. However, when using the joystick port for general interfacing it is probably better if these inputs are read directly. When using GW BASIC or Q BASIC this is achieved using the INP function, and the four "firebutton" inputs are at bits four to seven of address &H201. This is address 513 in normal decimal numbering. You have to read all four bits at once, plus the four unused bits of that address as well. It is a simple matter to mask off any unwanted bits though, so that you can effectively read only the bit or bits that are of interest to you. This is achieved using "bitwise" ANDing, which is a process that is described in detail later in this chapter.

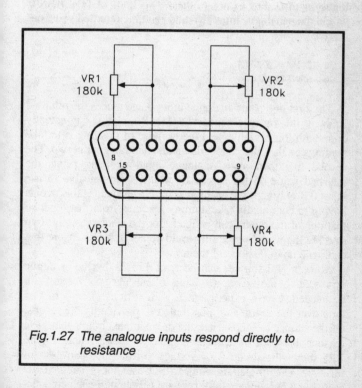

Fig.1.27 The analogue inputs respond directly to resistance

Analogue Reading

Reading the analogue inputs directly is probably not worthwhile, and it is much easier to exploit the built-in joystick reading functions of most high level PC languages. When using GW BASIC (or a compatible BASIC) it is the STICK function that is used to read the port. The STICK(0) function returns a value from channel 0 (i.e. analogue input 0), and it also results in readings being taken on the other three channels. These additional readings are stored in memory and can then be returned using the STICK(1), STICK(2), and STICK(3) functions. These read analogue inputs one to three respectively. The important point to note here is that analogue inputs one to three can only be read if a "dummy" reading is first taken from analogue input 0. For example, these two lines of GW BASIC would read analogue input two and print the returned value on-screen.

```
10   DUMMY = STICK(0)
20   PRINT STICK(2)
```

The first line reads analogue input 0 and places the returned value in the variable called "DUMMY". Nothing is actually done with this variable, and the purpose of this line is to take readings on the other analogue inputs, including input two. The second line then reads analogue input two and prints the returned value on the screen. It would seem sensible to use input 0 if only a single analogue input is needed, as this avoids having to continually take dummy readings from this input so that one of the others can be read. For the same reason, if two or three inputs are needed it would be advisable to ensure that analogue input 0 is one of them.

Some signal sources can be read directly by the analogue inputs, but in most cases a voltage-to-resistance conversion will be needed. I have experimented with various circuits of this type over the years, and most failed to provide usable results. Of the sundry methods tried, the only simple circuits that gave reasonable results were the ones based on opto-isolators. Figure 1.28 shows the circuit for a voltage-to-resistance converter of this type. The problem in using an opto-isolator is that the LED at its input has an unhelpful forward conduction characteristic.

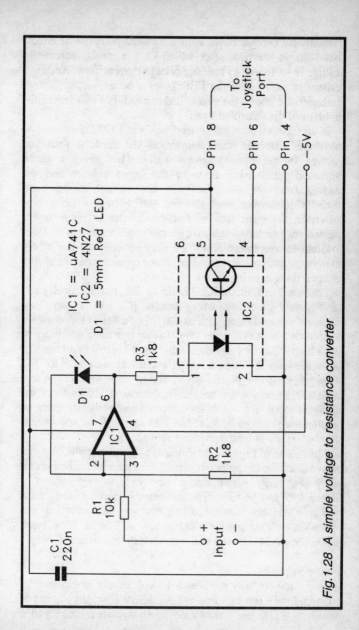

Fig. 1.28 A simple voltage to resistance converter

IC1 = uA741C
IC2 = 4N27
D1 = 5mm Red LED

To Joystick Port

Pin 8
Pin 6
Pin 4
-5V

D1
R3 1k8
IC1
R1 10k
R2 1k8
C1 220n
+ Input -

61

Virtually no current flows until a forward potential of almost two volts is reached, after which only a small increase in voltage is sufficient to produce a large current flow. Adding a resistor in series with the LED gives a better voltage/current characteristic above the two volt threshold, but still leaves the problem of the threshold itself.

In this circuit non-linear feedback via LED D1 is used to introduce distortion that counteracts the forward threshold voltage in the opto-isolator's LED. This gives a much improved relationship between the input voltage and the reading from the analogue port, but do not expect good linearity. However sophisticated the voltage-to-resistance converter, the basic lack of linearity in the analogue inputs themselves precludes their use in any application that requires absolute measurement. They are only suitable for use where relative measurement is required, and a high degree of stability and precision is unimportant.

I used a 5 millimetre RED LED for D1, but practically any LED should give satisfactory results. IC2 can be any "bog standard" opto-isolator, such as a 4N27 or a TIL111. It does not need to be a high efficiency type. In fact it is not a good idea to use a high efficiency device, as this would result in a very low full scale voltage. Using a low efficiency opto-isolator the full scale potential is typically about one to three volts. Note that increased input voltage results in decreased values from the analogue input. This could be corrected electronically using an inverter stage ahead of IC1, but it is easier if the software is simply written to take this factor into account.

The circuit of Figure 1.28 requires a –5 volt supply. This can be provided by the negative supply generator described previously (Fig.1.19). Alternatively, the single supply version of Figure 1.29 can be used. The operational amplifier used must be a type which is capable of single supply d.c. operation, and operation on a supply potential as low as 5 volts. Most types (LF351N, µA741C, etc.) will not work in this circuit.

Power Supplies

Where a project only requires a +5 volt supply at a current of no more than a few hundred milliamps, the most simple way of powering it is to use one of the +5 volt outputs on the joystick

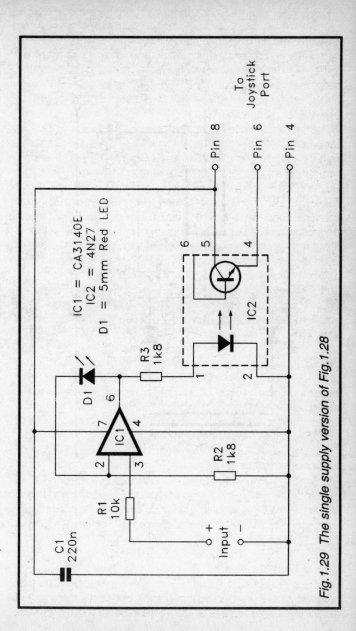

IC1 = CA3140E
IC2 = 4N27
D1 = 5mm Red LED

To Joystick Port

Pin 8
Pin 6
Pin 4

Fig.1.29 The single supply version of Fig.1.28

63

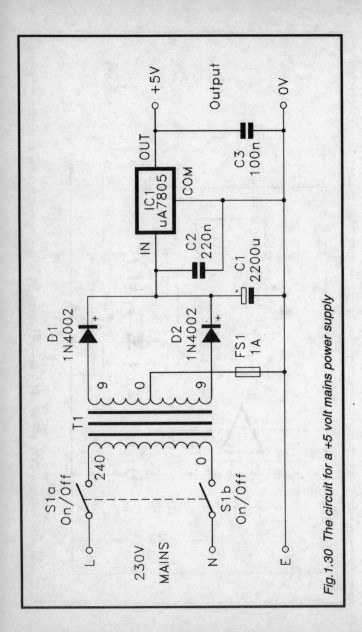

Fig.1.30 The circuit for a +5 volt mains power supply

64

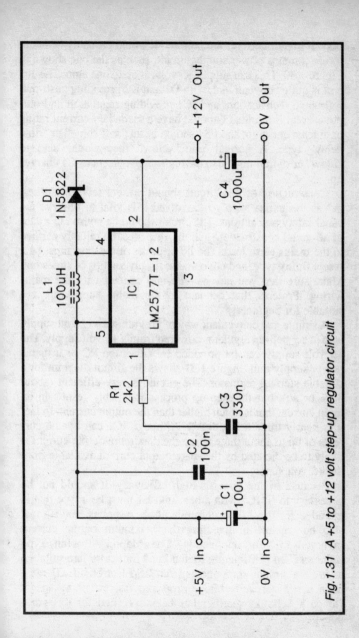

Fig.1.31 A +5 to +12 volt step-up regulator circuit

port. If higher currents are required it would probably be better to use a mains power supply circuit, such as the one shown in Figure 1.30. This can supply +5 volts at up to one amp. The circuit is quite conventional, with D1 and D2 providing push-pull full-wave rectification, and IC1 providing regulation and output current limiting. T1 should have a secondary current rating of at least one amp, and FS1 should be an "anti-surge" or "time delay" type. A normal "quick-blow" fuse would tend to "blow" at switch-on due to the high surge current as C1 charges up.

Construction of this circuit should present few difficulties, but as the mains supply is involved it is vital to observe the usual safety precautions. The circuit should be housed in a case of all-metal construction, and the case must be reliably earthed to the mains earth lead. The lid or cover of the case must be a screw fitting type, and not one that simply unclips or slides out. Make sure that you never come into contact with the mains wiring. Projects that connect to the mains supply are not suitable for beginners.

A simple and convenient way of providing a +12 volt supply is to use a step-up regulator powered from a +5 volt supply. The +5 volt supply can be provided by either the PC or a mains power supply unit. Figure 1.31 shows the circuit diagram for a suitable step-up regulator. The circuit is very efficient (about 80% or so), but the step-up process inevitably results in an input current that is much higher than the output current. In fact it is nearly three times higher. Although IC1 can handle currents of up to about three amps, the maximum output current is likely to be dictated by the spare output current available from the +5 volt supply.

Because of the circuit's high efficiency, it should not be necessary to fit IC1 with a heatsink. L1 must be a type that is intended for use in switch mode power supplies, and it must also be capable of handling the maximum output current involved in your application. The Maplin "Bobbin Type Inductors" and "Miniature Radial Lead Inductors" are suitable, as are the similar components from RS/Electromail. D1 must have a low forward voltage drop and fast switching speed. Hence a Schottky rectifier has been specified for this component.

Bitwise ANDing

There is a slight problem when reading handshake inputs, in that you wish to know the state of just one line of an eight bit input port. The computer can only read all eight bits at once, and has no means of reading a selected bit. Some means of processing the returned value to mask off the other seven bits is needed. This would effectively be the same as only reading the bit that is of interest. The standard way of doing this, and the one used in many of the example programs in this book, is to use the bitwise AND function. This function is available in most PC languages (including GW BASIC), and is available when using machine code or assembly language. Although bitwise ANDing is often crucial when writing software for use with your add-ons, it is not one of the most widely understood aspects of programming. Therefore, to end this chapter we will consider the basics of this simple but important programming technique.

Basically all you have to do is bitwise AND the value returned from the input port with the correct masking number. The correct masking number is the one that will permit the required bit or bits to be read, while masking the other bits so that they have no effect on the answer. The masking number is easy to calculate, and the table at the end of this chapter makes things even easier. Simply look up the masking number for the bit you wish to read. If you wish to read several bits, look up the masking number for each one, and then add these numbers together. For example, suppose that you wish to read a status output connected to bit three of an input port. As you can see from the table, the correct masking number for bit three is eight. This simple GW BASIC program will read the input port at address &H379, bitwise AND the returned value with a masking number of 8, and then print the answer on the screen.

```
10    REM MASKING PROGRAM TO READ BIT THREE
20    X = INP(&H379)
30    X = X AND 8
40    PRINT X
```

The value printed on the screen is zero if the relevant input line is low, and it is equal to the masking number (which is obviously eight in this case) if it is high. If you wished to read bits six and seven, a masking number of 192 would be used (64 plus 128 = 192). The value returned from these bits would be zero if they were both low, 64 if bit six was low and bit seven was high, 128 if bit seven was high and bit six was low, or 192 if both bits were high.

In practice the ANDed value is often used in a conditional instruction. The status output of the analogue to digital converter described previously is a good example of this. When using this output the program has to continuously test the state of status output, and simply loop continuously while a value of 0 is returned. Once a non-zero value is detected, the program moves on to the next routine and reads the converter. Bitwise ANDing is crucial when using four handshake inputs of the printer port to input bytes as two nibbles. It is obviously essential to read only the relevant four bits, and effectively eliminate the other four bits.

In order to fully understand the bitwise ANDing process you need to consider the two values on a bit-by-bit basis. If a bit is set to one in both the returned value and the masking number, a one will be placed in that bit of the answer. If either or both bits are set to zero, a zero is placed in that bit of the answer. Consequently, by using zero in a bit of the masking number, you ensure that a zero is placed in that bit of the answer, and that the relevant bit is masked. Using one in a bit of the masking number does not force a particular result in that bit of the answer. The relevant bit will be set to the same state as that bit of the returned value, enabling that bit to be read.

Table of Masking Numbers

Input Bit	Masking Number
0	1
1	2
2	4
3	8
4	16
5	32
6	64
7	128

Chapter 2

EASY INTERFACING PROJECTS

In Chapter 1 the basics of interfacing to the PC printer and joystick ports were considered. In this chapter we will consider some practical interfacing techniques, plus some projects that connect to these ports. We will start with projects that utilize the analogue input port described in Chapter 1. The first project is a temperature sensor which covers a range of zero to 100 degrees Celsius with a resolution of 0.5 degrees.

Matter of Degree

There are numerous sensors that can be used to detect temperature changes, but not all of them are well suited to temperature measurement. In order to keep things reasonably simple and straightforward it is necessary to have a sensor that provides good linearity over the full temperature range to be covered by the system. Semiconductor sensors are usually the best choice if very high and very low temperatures are not involved.

Semiconductor temperature sensors rely on the fact that the voltage across a forward biased silicon diode varies with changes in temperature. The voltage across a forward biased silicon diode is about 0.65 volts, but increases in temperature produce a reduction of about two or three millivolts per degree Celsius. Changes in the forward current produce small changes in output voltage, but this effect can be eliminated by feeding the diode from a constant current source. Although the voltage change per degree Celsius is not very large, only a small amount of amplification is needed in order to provide an output voltage swing that is adequate for most purposes. The linearity is usually very good over a large temperature range, and many practical semiconductor temperature sensors cover a range of 100 degrees Celsius or more.

A slight problem with a basic diode temperature sensor is that it produces a large offset voltage. For example, over a zero to 100 degree range the output voltage from a diode might vary between 0.7 and 0.5 volts. This compares with a basic input voltage range of zero to 2.55 volts for a ZN448E series analogue to digital converter. In order to interface a diode sensor to this converter it is necessary to remove the 0.5 volt offset voltage, and provide some amplification. It is also helpful if the signal is inverted, so that rises in temperature produce increased and not reduced output voltage. This inversion is not absolutely essential though, since it can effectively be provided by the software.

It is not actually all that difficult to provide this signal conditioning, but these days it is easier to use an integrated circuit temperature sensor that has built-in circuits to provide the necessary level shifting, etc. The LM35DZ conveniently provides an output voltage of 10 millivolts (0.01 volts) per degree Celsius with no offset voltage at all. This device was probably designed for use with digital multimeters and digital voltmeter modules to provide an easy way of using them as thermometers. However, it is equally suitable for use with a computer and an analogue to digital converter.

The LM35DZ covers a temperature range of zero to 100 degrees Celsius (–40 to +110 degrees Celsius for the otherwise identical LM35CZ). The supply voltage range is four to 30 volts, and with a current consumption of only about 56 microamps there is minimal self-heating. Although this sensor seems ideally suited to use with a ZN448E, which has a resolution of 10 millivolts, things are not quite that simple. The output voltage range of the LM35DZ is zero to one volt, which compares to an input voltage range of zero to 2.55 volts for the ZN448E. This would effectively be using the ZN448E as something less than a seven bit converter, rather than an eight bit type. The resolution of the system would be one degree Celsius, which is inadequate for most purposes.

Better results are obtained if the output from the LM35DZ is amplified and then fed to the input of the ZN448E. Amplification by a factor of two provides an output voltage range of zero to two volts (or 2.2 volts for the LM35CZ), which makes much better use of the converter's resolution. It still falls slightly short of providing full eight bit resolution, but the shortfall is not a serious one. In practical applications of analogue to digital converters it is often necessary to make minor compromises of this type. The temperature resolution of the system is a more useful 0.5 degrees Celsius.

If the full temperature range is not required it is possible to obtain a further improvement in the resolution. For example, amplifying the output of the LM35DZ by a factor of four provides an output voltage range of zero to four volts. The ZN448E can only handle input potentials of up to 2.55 volts, which would limit the operating temperature range of the system to zero to 63.75 degrees. This reduced maximum operating temperature would still be adequate for many purposes, and the resolution of the system would then be a very useful 0.25 degrees. Using an amplifier having a voltage gain of five times would give a maximum operating temperature of 51 degrees, and a resolution of 0.2 degrees Celsius.

Thermometer Circuits
The LM35DZ is a three terminal device which has a standard TO92 plastic encapsulation, and it is very simple to use. The supply voltage is applied to two leadout wires and the output voltage is taken from the third. Figure 2.1 provides connection details for this device. Although the LM35DZ has a transistor style encapsulation, Figure 2.1 follows the convention for integrated circuit pinout diagrams, and shows the device viewed

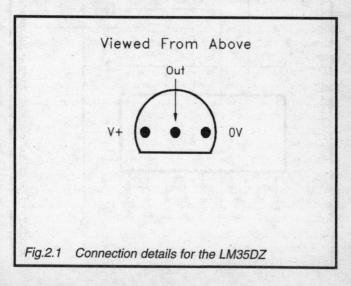

Fig.2.1   Connection details for the LM35DZ

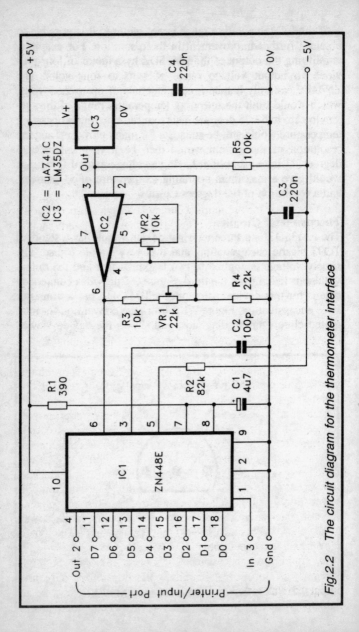

Fig.2.2 The circuit diagram for the thermometer interface

72

from above (i.e. viewed with the leadout wires pointing away from you).

Figure 2.2 shows the circuit diagram for a temperature interface based on an LM35DZ and a ZN448E. Note that the digital outputs of the converter must be interfaced to the PC's printer port via a suitable circuit (e.g. the circuit of Figure 1.9 in Chapter 1). IC3 is the temperature sensor and IC2 is the amplifier stage. VR2 is the offset null control for IC2, and it is also used to deal with the minor offset voltage problem of IC1. R3, VR1 and R4 are the negative feedback network for IC2, and VR1 is adjusted to provide a voltage gain of two. In practice, VR2 is adjusted for optimum accuracy at a low temperature, and VR1 is set for optimum accuracy at a high temperature. If this process is repeated two or three times the system should provide good accuracy over the full temperature range.

The maximum operating temperature is increased to 110 degree Celsius if an LM35CZ is used for IC3. Although the LM35CZ can handle temperatures down to −40 degrees Celsius, temperatures below zero provide a negative output voltage which the converter can not handle. Thus, even when using the LM35CZ, the minimum operating temperature remains zero. If operation over a restricted temperature range with higher resolution is required, reduce the value of R4 to 6k8. This will enable IC2 to be set for a closed loop voltage gain of four or five times, giving a resolution of 0.25 or 0.2 degrees Celsius respectively.

One slight problem with this interface is that it requires a −5 volt supply. This could be supplied from a +5 volt supply using the simple negative supply generator circuit featured in Chapter 1 (Figure 1.19). However, there would be a slight risk that the loaded output voltage of this circuit would be insufficient to permit the output of IC2 to reach zero volts. The switch mode power supply of Figure 2.3 is a safer option. This is a conventional inverter circuit based on a TL497N switch mode power supply chip. VR1 controls the output voltage, and is obviously adjusted for an output potential of −5 volts.

D1 could be a Schottky rectifier such as a 1N5822, but high efficiency is not crucial in this application where only low output currents (a few milliamps) are involved. L1 must be an inductor which is intended for use in switch mode power

73

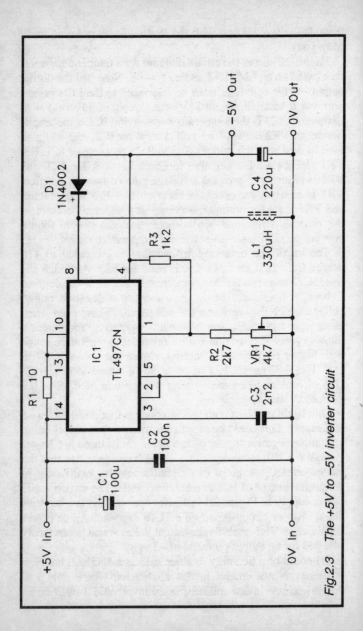

Fig.2.3 The +5V to −5V inverter circuit

supplies, and not an r.f. choke. The Maplin 330µH "Miniature Radial Lead Inductor" is suitable, as is the RS/Electromail 330µH "Low Current Radial Inductor". R1 is part of the current limiting circuit at the input of IC1. This limits the maximum output current to about 15 milliamps, which is adequate in this case. For higher output currents the value of R1 can be reduced to one ohm. This enables the circuit to provide output currents of up to about 150 milliamps. Bear in mind though, that the efficiency of this circuit is less than 50 percent. Consequently, with an output current of 150 milliamps the input current will be nearly 350 milliamps.

If a high degree of accuracy at low temperatures is not required, the single supply temperature interface of Figure 2.4 can be used. This is basically the same as the original circuit, but IC2 has been changed from a µA741C to a CA3140E, and the negative supply has been omitted. The offset null control (VR2) has been retained, and the setting up procedure for this circuit remains the same as that for the original version.

The temperature interface circuit of Figure 2.5 shows an alternative method of tackling IC1's minor offset voltage problem. Instead of using an offset null control for IC1, a passive mixer at the output of the amplifier is used to introduce a small positive offset voltage to the output signal of IC2. As before, VR1 is used to calibrate the circuit at a high temperature, and VR2 is used to calibrate the circuit at a low temperature. This method of providing the converter with a suitable offset voltage is applicable whenever an input amplifier or buffer stage is used.

Calibration
It is normal with this type of equipment for the temperature sensor to be fitted into some sort of probe assembly. Apart from making everything much neater, this also protects IC1, and the connections to it, from moisture in the air, etc. Note that some sort of protective casing is essential if the sensor is to be used in liquids. In addition to protecting IC1 from the liquid, this is also necessary to prevent signals from IC1's leadouts passing through the liquid. This would upset the operation of the circuit, and due to an electrolytic action it could also alter any liquid into which IC1 was placed.

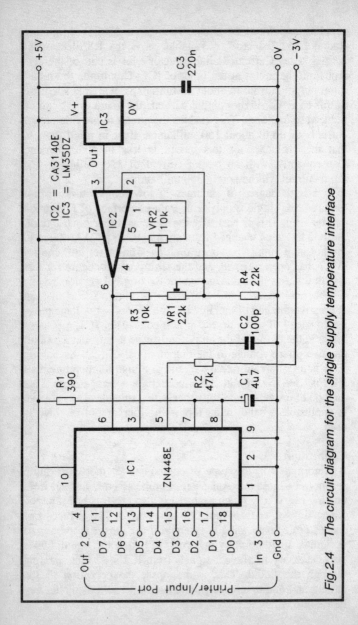

Fig.2.4   The circuit diagram for the single supply temperature interface

76

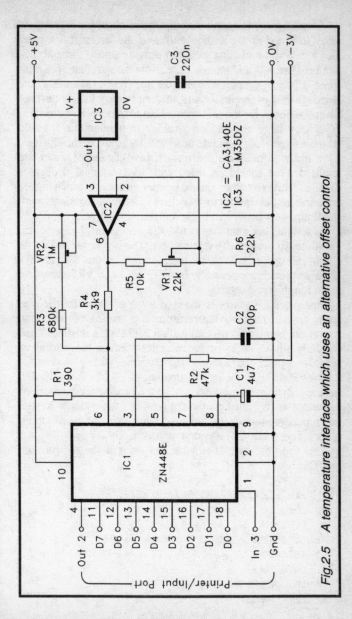

Fig.2.5 A temperature interface which uses an alternative offset control

77

A small glass test tube makes a good basis for a probe. In order to speed up the response time of the sensor it is a good idea to use some silicone grease to provide a good thermal contact between IC1 and the test tube. Note though, that even with some silicone grease included in the probe assembly, the response time of the sensor will still not be very fast. It can take several seconds for the sensor to adjust to temperature changes. With very large and sudden changes in temperature it could take the sensor half a minute or so to fully adjust to the changes.

In order to calibrate the system two glasses of water are required. One should be filled with iced water at 0 degrees Celsius, while the other should contain water at a much higher temperature (around 50 to 70 degrees Celsius). Accidents with small amounts of water in this temperature range are unlikely to be serious, but a mishap could still be a painful experience. Treat the hot water with due respect. The hot water should be monitored using an accurate thermometer so that you always know its precise temperature. Initially, VR1 and VR2 should be set at roughly mid settings.

First place the sensor in the cold water and wait for the sensor to adjust to the low temperature. If a reading of more than zero is not being obtained, adjust VR2 for such a reading. Then carefully adjust VR2 just far enough to reduce the reading to zero. Next place the sensor in the hot water and again wait for it to settle down at the new temperature. VR1 is then adjusted for the correct reading, after noting the precise temperature of the water as indicated on the calibration thermometer. Repeat this procedure two or three times to make sure that everything is set up accurately. The system is then ready for use.

This short program is suitable for use with the temperature interface.

```
10   REM THERMOMETER PROGRAM (0 TO 100 DEGREES)
20   CLS
30   OUT &H37A,4
40   OUT &H37A,0
50   OUT &H37A,4
60   OUT &H37A,5
70   LSN = INP(&H379) AND 240
80   LSN = LSN/16
```

```
90    OUT &H37A,4
100   MSN = INP(&H379) AND 240
110   BYTE = LSN + MSN
120   BYTE = BYTE/2
130   CLS
140   PRINT BYTE" DEGREES CELSIUS"
150   FOR DELAY = 1 TO 30000
160   NEXT DELAY
170   A$ = INKEY$
180   IF LEN(A$) = 0 THEN GOTO 30
```

Line 20 clears the screen, and then lines 30 to 110 read the
analogue to digital converter. As usual, it is assumed that the
converter is read via an input port which uses bits four to seven,
with a hardware inversion on bit 7. The start conversion input
of the converter must be driven from "Out 2", and the end of
conversion output is not monitored because the program will
not run fast enough to produce premature readings of the converter. At line 120 the value read from the converter is divided
by two, which is the only additional mathematics needed to
produce an answer in degrees Celsius. Of course, if you are
using 0.25 or 0.2 degree resolution, the correct division rate is
four or five (respectively).

The screen is cleared at line 130, and then the temperature
followed by "DEGREES CELSIUS" is printed at the top of the
screen. After a short delay provided by lines 150 and 160, the
program is looped back to line 30 where another reading is
commenced. The program therefore loops indefinitely, printing
an updated temperature reading at the top of the screen every
couple of seconds. The loop rate is largely dependent on the
speed of the PC used, so a lower value at line 150 might be
better if you have a slow PC, or a higher value might be better
if you have the latest thing in "turbo" PCs. The last two lines of
the program provide a means of breaking out of the program.
Pressing any character key will give A$ as a length of other
than zero, and bring the program to an end. Due to the delay at
lines 150 and 160 it may take a second or two for this to
happen.

Voltage Measurement

Voltage measurement using a computer might seem to be an "over the top" method of handling things, and for many voltage measurement applications I suppose it would be. On the other hand, a computerised voltage measuring system can be programmed to automatically take readings at preset intervals. Alternatively, the system can constantly monitor voltages, record the results, and sound an alarm if readings stray outside certain limits. A variety of similar monitoring applications are possible. This type of monitoring is more than a little helpful where newly designed circuits must be tested for short to medium term stability, or when trying to trace the problem in a piece of electronic equipment that has an intermittent fault. Manual checking and monitoring in these circumstances can take a vast amount of man-hours, and can be a bit tedious for whoever gets the job of writing down all the results.

The analogue to digital converter circuit featured in Chapter 1 (Figure 1.23) can be used for voltage measurement, but its input voltage range of 0 to 5 volts is obviously unsuitable for many voltage monitoring purposes. As explained in Chapter 1, the full scale input voltage is easily altered, and this is a topic we will consider in more detail here. The values in the attenuator circuit at the input of the converter can be changed to suit other input sensitivities, but as explained previously, the parallel resistance through the two arms of the attenuator should be about 4k. With the specified values for R4 and R5 their parallel resistance is clearly 4k1. If the parallel resistance of the two attenuator resistors is not reasonably close to 4k it might not be possible to adjust VR1 for the correct offset, and accuracy at low input voltages will be fractionally less than optimum.

What this means in practice is that R4 will be lower in value for higher full scale input voltages. For example, a full scale voltage of 10.2 volts would require R4 to be reduced to 5k6, with R5 being increased to 16k8. This second value is not a preferred value, but it could be made up from a 15k resistor in series with a 1k8 component. Due to component tolerances, it will often be necessary to use a preset resistor in one arm of the attenuator so that the sensitivity of the circuit can be trimmed to precisely the required level. In this example a 10k fixed resistor in series with a 10k preset could be used instead of R5.

A 20.4 volt full scale potential would require R4 to be even lower in value – say 4k7. The value of R5 would need to be seven times this value (32k9) in order to give the required amount of attenuation. On the face of it I have made an error here, as the required full scale potential is some eight times higher than the 2.55 volt full scale sensitivity of the converter ($2.55 \times 8 = 20.4$), and not seven times this value. The salient point here is that for every volt developed across R4, seven volts must be produced across R5. For every eight volts across the entire resistor network, one volt will then be developed across R4, giving the required eight to one attenuation ratio. The correct value for the input resistance is therefore equal to the value of R4 multiplied by one less than the required attenuation factor. Again, the value required is not a preferred value, and it would have to be made up from two or more resistors, or a fixed resistor and a preset could be used.

For full scale voltages of about 50 volts or more it would be necessary to reduce R4 to a value of 4k3. In theory there is no upper limit to the maximum input voltage that can be accommodated, but in reality you have to bear in mind the practical limitations of the components. Unless you use special high voltage types, the attenuator resistors are likely to impose a limit of about 250 volts (the retailer's catalogue should give maximum voltage ratings for the fixed and preset resistors they sell). You should not try to measure potentials of more than about 100 volts unless you are sure you know what you are doing, and all the necessary safety precautions are taken.

Adjustment

If a preset resistor is used in the attenuator, this should be used to set the correct full scale sensitivity before VR1 is adjusted for the proper offset voltage. Ideally the sensitivity adjustment should be done by feeding the circuit with an input voltage equal to the full scale value. It is then just a matter of adjusting the attenuator preset for a stable reading at the appropriate figure. Good accuracy should be obtained using any calibration voltage that is fairly close to the full scale value. For example, suppose that a full scale value of 5.1 volts is required. If the PC's +5 volt supply is measured at 4.96 volts, then this could be used as the calibration voltage, with the attenuator preset being adjusted for a stable reading of 4.96 volts.

In order to adjust VR1 properly it is necessary to feed an input voltage to the circuit that is equal to half the resolution of the circuit. In this case the resolution is 20 millivolts, and a voltage of 10 millivolts must therefore be fed to the input of the circuit. A suitable voltage can be provided using the simple potential divider network of Figure 2.6 plus the PC's +5 volt supply. With this circuit feeding into the input of the converter circuit, VR1 is adjusted for an unstable reading that fluctuates between 0 and 1. It is then a good idea to check the full scale accuracy of the circuit, and if necessary, recalibrate the unit again using the attenuator preset.

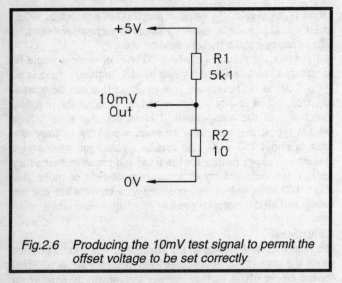

Fig.2.6   Producing the 10mV test signal to permit the offset voltage to be set correctly

It is worth mentioning that the offset errors are quite small. In fact the error is typically only 5 millivolts at the input of the converter, which compares with a resolution of 10 millivolts here. Obviously this error is quite small, but it is still significant on very low readings. Nevertheless, in some applications there may well be no point in bothering with the offset circuit. In particular, in some applications the minimum practical reading could well be somewhere around twenty to fifty percent of the full scale value, and the effect of the offset circuit could well be insignificant in such cases.

Software
This listing is for a program that will display the input voltage on the screen.

```
10    REM VOLTAGE READING PROGRAM
20    CLS
30    OUT &H37A,4
40    OUT &H37A,0
50    OUT &H37A,4
60    OUT &H37A,5
70    LSN = INP(&H379) AND 240
80    LSN = LSN/16
90    OUT &H37A,4
100   MSN = INP(&H379) AND 240
110   BYTE = LSN + MSN
120   BYTE = BYTE/50
130   CLS
140   PRINT BYTE" VOLTS"
150   FOR DELAY = 1 TO 30000
160   NEXT DELAY
170   A$ = INKEY$
180   IF LEN(A$) = 0 THEN GOTO 30
```

This program operates in the same basic fashion as the thermometer program described previously. Line 120 has been altered to give a division by 50 rather than 2. It is assumed here that the converter has a full scale value of 5.1 volts. Using a division of 50 gives the correct full scale value of 5.1 volts and a resolution of 20 millivolts (0.02 volts). If a different full scale voltage is used, the division rate used in line 120 must be altered to suit. For example, the division rate would be 25 for a full scale value of 10.2 volts. It is advisable to use a full scale voltage that is an exact multiple of 2.55 volts, as this gives sensible voltage readings. If you use an odd resolution such as 27.3798 millivolts, you will end up with some odd looking voltage readings! The only other change to the program is to print the word "VOLTS" instead of "DEGREES CELSIUS" at line 140.

In some applications you may simply wish to have a program which, like this one, just displays readings. Remember though, that with a computerised measuring system there are almost endless possibilities. For example, readings can be taken at regular intervals, stored in memory, and displayed later in graph form. Another possibility is for readings to be taken at regular intervals and printed out on the system printer. This type of thing is useful for monitoring new circuits, or testing for intermittent faults. It is a matter of tailoring things to suit your particular application.

Buffered Input
The basic analogue to digital converter circuit is satisfactory for some purposes, but it only works well if it is fed from a fairly low source impedance. Like an ordinary analogue multimeter, it requires a significant input current. In analogue multimeter terms, it has a rather poor sensitivity of only about 2k to 3k per volt. This can result in loading on a test point, and a substantial voltage reduction at that point while the measurement is being made. More consistent and reliable results can be obtained by adding a buffer stage ahead of the converter. This gives a very high input resistance, and a minimal input current. Like a high resistance analogue voltmeter or a digital multimeter, this ensures that there is no significant loading on the circuit under test, and that accurate results are obtained.

Figure 2.7 shows the circuit diagram for a buffer stage that can be added ahead of this converter to provide a much higher input resistance. The input resistance of the MOSFET operational amplifier used in the circuit is over a million megohms, but in practice the circuit as a whole has a substantially lower input resistance. This is due to the need for bias and attenuation resistors at the input, which shunt the input resistance down to what is typically about 10 megohms or so. This is clearly a massive reduction on the basic input resistance of the operational amplifier, but it is still high enough to give good results when the unit is used to make measurements on normal circuits.

The circuit is basically just a non-inverting amplifier with 100% negative feedback so that it has unity voltage gain. VR2

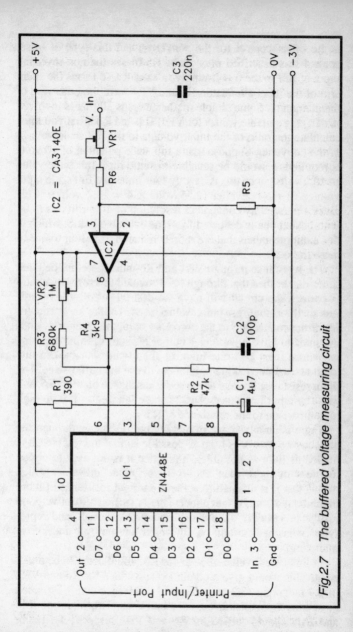

Fig.2.7 The buffered voltage measuring circuit

85

is the offset control for the converter, and this type of offset control was described previously. R5 biases the non-inverting input of IC1 to the 0 volt supply rail and it also forms the shunt arm of the input attenuator. R6 and VR1 form the other arm of the attenuator. Some simple mathematics is all that is involved in deriving suitable values for VR1, R5, and R6. First you must calculate the ratio of the input voltage to the full scale voltage of the converter. Suppose that a full scale potential of 10 volts is required. It would be sensible to settle for a full scale value of 10.2 volts, since this is exactly four times the full scale input voltage of the converter (2.55 volts × 4 = 10.2 volts). This gives a reasonably convenient resolution of 40 millivolts (0.04 volts). Next one is deducted from the calculated ratio, which in this example means that the ratio is reduced from four to one to three to one.

The resistance through VR1 and R6 must therefore be three times higher than that through R5. Provided this resistance ratio is correct, the circuit will have the desired sensitivity, regardless of the actual resistance values used. Unlike an attenuator for direct connection to the converter chip, this attenuator does not need to have a particular output resistance. In practice the resistance must be quite high, or the circuit will have a low input resistance, making it pointless to use the buffer stage. The input resistance is equal to the series resistance of VR1, R5, and R6. The input resistance of IC2 can be ignored as it is so high in comparison to the resistance of R5.

There is an advantage in making the resistance through the attenuator network as high as possible so that the test circuit is loaded as little as possible. In practice it is not easy to obtain resistors of more than about 10 megohms in value, which means that it is difficult to achieve an input resistance of more than about 10 to 20 megohms. This is sufficient to give good results in virtually all practical situations though, and represents what will often be an input current of under one microamp.

In this case a value of 3M3 for R5 would seem to be about right. This would give a combined resistance for R6 and VR1 of 9.9 megohms (3.3 megohms × 3 = 9.9 megohms). Provided close tolerance resistors are used for R5 and R6, values of 9M1 and 2M2 should suffice for R6 and VR1 respectively. Using ordinary 10% resistors this set of values might not give a wide enough adjustment range to permit the correct full scale value to be set. Values of 8M2 and 4M7 would then be a better choice. However, in the interest of good long term stability it is better to use good quality resistors, and to have the value of VR1 fairly low in relation to that of R6.

Adjustment

Adjustment starts with offset voltage control VR2. In order to set this correctly it is necessary to feed in an input voltage that is equal to 0.5 l.s.b., which in this example is 20 millivolts (0.02 volts). This can be derived from the +5 volt supply using the potential divider circuit of Figure 2.8. It is then just a matter of

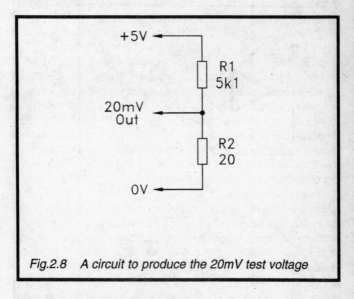

Fig.2.8   A circuit to produce the 20mV test voltage

adjusting VR2 for a setting that causes the value returned from the port to fluctuate between zero and one (which will be displayed as voltage readings of zero and 0.04 volts). The input of the circuit is then connected to an accurately known potential that represents about 70 to 100 percent of the full scale value. VR1 is then adjusted for the appropriate voltage reading.

Over-Voltage Protection

In some voltage measuring applications there is no significant risk of an excessive input voltage causing damage to the input amplifier and the converter. In others there is a strong risk of this happening, and it is then essential to include a protection circuit ahead of IC2. The easiest way of doing this is to add a zener diode in parallel with R5, as shown in Figure 2.9. This clips the input voltage at 5.6 volts, which is low enough to ensure that IC2 is safe. At voltages of 2.55 volts or less the resistance of D1 should be so high that it does not significantly shunt R5 and affect the accuracy of the circuit. D1 also

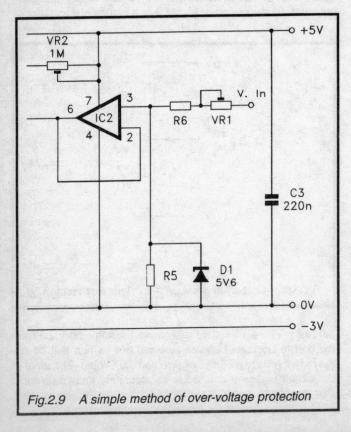

Fig.2.9   A simple method of over-voltage protection

88

provides protection against reverse voltages. These cause it to conduct in the forward direction. It then operates much like an ordinary silicon diode and clips the input signal at about –0.7 volts.

Low Voltage Measurement

It is possible to measure quite low voltages if the converter circuit is preceded by a d.c. amplifier. I would not recommend trying to use high levels of gain to measure really small voltages if this can be avoided. There are two main problems when using sensitive d.c. measuring equipment, which are drift and noise problems. The problem of drift need not be a major one provided the operating temperature is reasonably stable. Also, there are special instrumentation grade operational amplifiers which can be used in applications where high d.c. stability is essential. These devices are relatively expensive though.

The noise problem can be a more difficult one to tackle. First there is the noise of the operational amplifier itself. In many cases this will not be severe enough to cause any major difficulties. However, one of the special low noise devices can be used where the innate noise of the amplifier becomes a major problem. These ultra low noise operational amplifiers are much more expensive than the "bog standard" types, but they can produce a reduction in the noise level by a factor of ten or more.

In my experience the main problem is caused by noise that is picked up at the input of the circuit by some form of stray coupling. This can be caused by earthing problems, or standard stray coupling to non-screened input wiring. Obviously this type of thing can be minimised by using a carefully designed layout, using good quality screened cables, etc., but it can be more difficult than you might think to eliminate the problem. Digital circuits, especially computers, produce large amounts of electrical noise which somehow seems to find its way into any nearby circuit that is operating at low signal levels.

Where low voltages really must be measured, a simple d.c. amplifier of the type shown in the interface circuit Figure 2.10 is needed. Although a µA741C is specified for IC2, the circuit should work properly using any genuinely µA741C compatible operational amplifier, such as a CA3140E or OP-77GP. Where high gain is used and optimum accuracy is needed, there is a

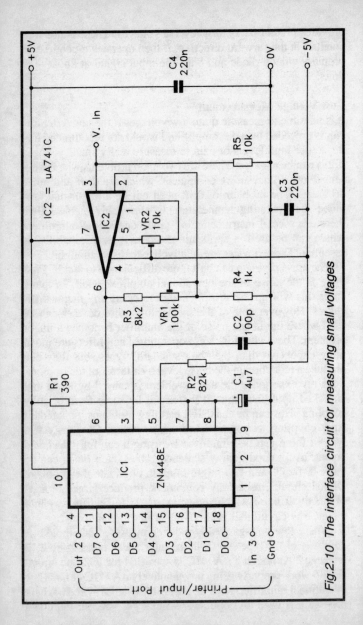

Fig.2.10 The interface circuit for measuring small voltages

definite advantage in using a precision operational amplifier such as an OP-07CN or an OP-77GP. The circuit is just a standard non-inverting mode amplifier having R5 as the input bias resistor and R3, R4, and VR1 as the negative feedback network. VR2 is the offset null control, and this is adjusted in the same manner as the offset null controls in some of the previous circuits.

The input resistance of the circuit is set by R5, and it is simply equal to whatever value is given to this component. This can be a megohm or more in value if desired, but it is advisable not to use a very high input resistance unless it is really necessary. A high input resistance can result in a relatively high noise level. With operational amplifiers that do not have a f.e.t. input stage of some kind it can also result in reduced precision. The gain of the circuit is equal to (R3 plus R4 plus VR1) divided by R4. VR1 enables the voltage gain to be varied from under 10 times to more than 100 times, which enables the circuit to handle most practical applications. The maximum closed loop voltage gain can be increased by making R4 lower in value, and a value of 100R would permit a maximum voltage gain of over 1000 times. However, the higher the gain of the circuit, the greater the likelihood of problems with noise, drift, and large offset voltages. High voltage gains certainly require the use of a high quality precision operational amplifier.

The bandwidth of the amplifier is quite wide using most operational amplifiers, and is actually equal to the gain bandwidth product of the operational amplifier divided by the closed loop voltage gain (i.e. the voltage gain set using VR1). Even for the inexpensive μA741C the gain bandwidth product is 1MHz, which means that it provides a bandwidth of 10 to 100kHz at voltage gains from 100 to 10 times. Many modern operation amplifiers provide a bandwidth about 3 to 10 times wider than the standard μA741C. This is far more than is really needed in many applications.

The excess bandwidth does not matter, but it can be beneficial to reduce the bandwidth if noise is proving to be problematic. The easiest way to do this is to add a filter capacitor in parallel with R3 and VR1. This gives increased feedback at high frequencies, and rolls-off the amplifier's frequency response. In many applications the rate at which readings are taken is quite slow, and the rate at which input voltages change is even slower. This permits quite a large filter capacitor (about 1µ) to be used, possibly giving a bandwidth of no more than a few hertz. This would give a substantial reduction in the noise level.

Current Measurement

In theory it is quite easy to measure current using a computer plus an analogue to digital converter. The basic method used is shown in Figure 2.11. This really just consists of a resistor added across the input of the analogue to digital converter circuit. The current flow through the resistor is proportional to the applied voltage, and readings from the converter are therefore easily converted into corresponding current flows. For example, if R1 is given a value of 1k, a full scale potential of 2.55 volts will produce a current flow of 2.55 milliamps (2.55 volts divided by 1000 ohms = 0.00255 amps, or 2.55 milliamps). Readings from the converter can therefore be converted into milliamps simply by dividing them by 100. This table shows the resistor values required for some useful full scale currents.

Resistance	Full Scale Current
1R	2.55 amps
10R	255 milliamps
100R	25.5 milliamps
1k	2.55 milliamps
10k	255 microamps

Higher values will give greater sensitivity, but the input resistance of the converter could significantly shunt the input resistor, giving poor accuracy. An input buffer amplifier would be needed to avoid this problem. Note that values such as 1R, 10R, etc., give readings from the converter that are easily converted into current readings. Values such as 4k7, 22R, etc., are usable, but would be inconvenient in practice. You could easily find yourself with a system that measures currents in increments such as 1.563 milliamps!

Although this method of current measurement is fine in theory, there are one or two important points to keep in mind when using such a setup in practice. One of these is simply that

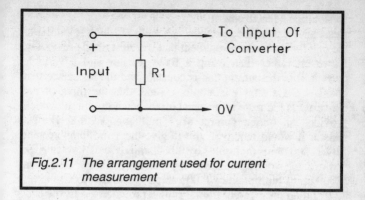

Fig.2.11 The arrangement used for current measurement

adding R1 into the current path will often have a significant effect on the current flow. Bear in mind that there can be a voltage drop of up to 2.55 volts across R1, which could be very significant in many cases. It is not a good idea to connect the output of R1 to the ZN448E via an attenuator and offset circuit, as this would increase the voltage drop introduced by the circuit.

In general, the addition of R1 in the current path will inevitably result in some reduction in the current that flows. It should perhaps be pointed out that this problem is not unique to this system, and it also affects all but the most sophisticated of current measuring techniques. To minimise this problem an amplifier can be added ahead of the converter. All that is needed is a circuit of the type shown in Figure 2.10 and described in the previous section of this book. If the circuit is set for a closed loop voltage gain of ten times, the value of R1 can be reduced by a factor of 10. Of no less importance, the maximum voltage drop through the circuit is reduced by a factor of 10, which means that the maximum voltage drop through R1 becomes just 255 millivolts (0.255 volts).

The second point to keep in mind is that the negative input terminal is connected to earth. This is not normally a problem when measuring voltages, where it is usually the voltage with respect to earth that must be measured. With current measurement though, it is often necessary to measure currents where neither input terminal will be at earth potential. Unfortunately, this circuit is unsuitable for measurements of this type.

Resistance Measurement

Resistance can be measured using a method which is similar to the one for current measurement that was described previously. However, rather than using a fixed resistor and a variable current, it is the current that is constant and the resistance that changes. As a simple example, assume that the input of the converter is fed from a constant current generator circuit which provides an output current of 1 milliamp. With a 1k test resistor it would require 1 volt to give the 1 milliamp current flow (1000 ohms multiplied by 0.001 amps equals 1 volt). A 2k test resistor would produce an input to the converter of 2 volts (2000 ohms multiplied by 0.001 amps equals 2 volts).

It should be apparent from this that, provided a sensible current level is chosen, there is no difficulty in converting readings from the converter into corresponding resistance readings. In this example it is merely necessary to multiply by ten in order to produce readings in ohms, or to divide by 100 in order to give readings in kilohms. This table shows some test currents and the full scale resistance ranges that they provide with the 2.55 volt full scale voltage of the ZN448E converter.

Current	Full Scale Resistance
10mA	255R
1mA	2.55k
100µA	25.5k
10µA	255k
1µA	2.55M
0.1µA	25.5M

Figure 2.12 shows the circuit diagram for a resistance meter circuit that is based on the system outlined here. This design has been "borrowed" from the book "Electronic Projects For Your PC" (BP320), which is from the same publisher and author as this publication. TR1 operates in a conventional constant current generator circuit, which includes D1 to provide temperature compensation. S1 provides four switched emitter resistances, which give output currents of 1mA, 100µA, 10µA, and 1µA (corresponding to full scale values of 2.55k, 25.5k, 255k, and 2.55M). VR1 provides the highest current – VR4 provides the lowest current. Using preset resistors enables the unit to be set up for good accuracy on each range.

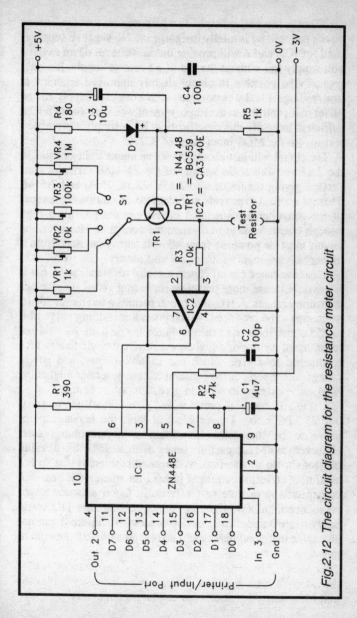

Fig.2.12 The circuit diagram for the resistance meter circuit

95

IC2 acts as a buffer amplifier which ensures that the loading on the test resistor is totally insignificant. No negative supply is used for IC2, and it will provide output voltages down to the 0 volt supply rail without the aid of a negative supply. It would probably be possible to obtain slightly improved accuracy at low readings if IC2 was provided with a negative supply and an offset null control, but the improvement would probably not be sufficient to justify this modification. R3 is simply a protection resistor for the MOS input stage of IC2.

The circuit will just about provide an output voltage equal to the 2.55 volt full scale voltage of the ZN448E series of converters, giving ranges of 0 to 2.55k, 25.5k, 255k, and 2.55M. There is no need to provide any overload protection at the input of the converter, because this circuit can not provide a high enough output voltage to damage the converter. However, the circuit must be powered from +5 volt supply, and not from a higher voltage supply such as a 9 volt battery.

This four range circuit covers a useful resistance span, but it is possible to use more preset resistors to give the unit further measuring ranges. A 100 ohm preset permits a test current of 10 milliamps to be produced, which gives a measuring range of 0 to 255 ohms, increasing the resolution to one ohm. I would not recommend the use of a higher test current though, unless TR1 is changed to a type which has suitable current and power ratings. Other parts of the constant current generator might also need some changes in order to give satisfactory results.

Using a 10 megohm preset would give a measuring range of 0 to 25.5 megohms. One problem in doing this is that it might prove to be impossible to obtain a 10 megohm preset. However, a 4M7 preset in series with a 4M7 fixed value resistor should be satisfactory. A second problem is that with a maximum collector current of just 0.1 microamps TR1 can not be expected to operate very efficiently. Good accuracy might be obtained, but any slight leakage current through TR1 could easily cause a significant loss of linearity. Therefore, I can not guarantee that good results will be obtained on a 25.5 megohm range.

Software

The software for this device presents no major difficulty. It is just a matter of doing some simple mathematics to suit the range in use, and displaying "KILOHMS", or "MEGOHMS" after the value printed on the screen. For example, on the 0 to 25.5k range the value returned from the converter must be divided by 10 to give an answer in kilohms, and the word "KILOHMS" or just "k" should obviously be displayed after the value. It is a good idea to include a routine that will detect a returned value of 255 and display an "Overload" warning on the screen. A value of 255 does not necessarily mean that the input voltage to the converter has gone beyond the full scale value, but in most cases this will be what has happened, and an overload has to be assumed. Note that with no resistor connected to the circuit a reading of 255 will be returned from the converter.

This simple GW BASIC program provides the bare necessities for a resistance meter program. Lines 30 and 40 set variables Y and B$ at their initial values of 100 and "k". Y is the number by which the returned values are divided, and this is either 1, 10, or 100, depending on the range in use. B$ is the units indicator, which is either "k" or "M" (or "kilohms" and "megohms" if you prefer). The initial values provide operation on range 1 (0 to 2.55k).

In order to change range the numeric keys from "1" to "4" are used. Pressing a key selects the appropriate range (e.g. pressing the "3" key selects range 3, which measures from 0 to 255k). A key press is detected by lines 140 and 150, which then take the program to a subroutine. The subroutine uses a series of IF . . . . THEN statements to detect which key has been pressed, and to make any necessary changes to variables Y and B$. The program then loops normally, taking and displaying readings on the screen until another key is pressed. The program can be terminated by pressing the "5" key. This is detected by line 300 of the subroutine, which then halts the program with an END instruction. Lines 50 to 130 are the basic port reading routine which places the complete eight bit value read from the port in the variable called "BYTE". If line 170 detects a reading of 255 from the port it prints an overload warning at the top of the screen.

```
10    REM RESISTANCE METER PROGRAM
20    CLS
30    Y = 100
40    B$ = "k"
50    OUT &H37A,4
60    OUT &H37A,0
70    OUT &H37A,4
80    OUT &H37A,5
90    LSN = INP(&H379) AND 240
100   LSN = LSN/16
110   OUT &H37A,4
120   MSN = INP(&H379) AND 240
130   BYTE = LSN + MSN
140   A$ = INKEY$
150   IF LEN(A$) = 1 THEN GOSUB 220
160   CLS
170   IF BYTE = 255 THEN PRINT "POSSIBLE OVERLOAD!"
180   PRINT BYTE/Y B$
190   FOR DELAY = 1 TO 10000
200   NEXT DELAY
210   GOTO 50
220   IF ASC(A$) = 49 THEN Y = 100
230   IF ASC(A$) = 49 THEN B$ = "k"
240   IF ASC(A$) = 50 THEN Y = 10
250   IF ASC(A$) = 50 THEN B$ = "k"
260   IF ASC(A$) = 51 THEN Y = 1
270   IF ASC(A$) = 51 THEN B$ = "k"
280   IF ASC(A$) = 52 THEN Y = 100
290   IF ASC(A$) = 52 THEN B$ = "M"
300   IF ASC(A$) = 53 THEN END
310   RETURN
```

Calibration

Four precision resistors having a tolerance of 1% or better are
needed in order to accurately calibrate the unit. These should
have values that are close to the full scale values of the four
ranges. Resistors of 2k2, 22k, 220k, and 2M2 in value are good
choices. Start with all four presets at approximately two-thirds
of maximum resistance. Switch the unit to the 2.55k range and

connect the 2k2 calibration resistor to the input terminals. Then adjust VR1 for a reading of 2.20 kilohms. Repeat the same basic procedure on the other three ranges using the 22k, 220k, and 2M2 calibration resistors. The unit is then ready for use.

Remember that the unit must be switched to a suitable range, and that there must be some means of telling the software which range is in use. With the basic setup you have to manually select the range on both the interface and the computer. It is not difficult to implement automatic range sensing, but as it requires some additional digital inputs it would be necessary to base the unit on a dual eight bit input port.

The most simple method of providing this automatic sensing is to have an extra pole on the range switch. This can be used to drive four digital inputs in the manner shown in Figure 2.13. A software routine can read the inputs, and determine which range is in use by detecting which of the inputs has been taken high. This is a matter of changing the conditions in the IF . . . THEN instructions at lines 220 to 290, so that the "Y" and "B$" variables are controlled by the value returned from the input port used to monitor these lines. Line 300 would have to be retained in order to provide a means of breaking out of the program.

My preferred method of handling things would be to control the resistance range from the computer using some of the otherwise unused digital outputs of the printer port. Fully electronic switching is one way of handling the switching, but there can be practical problems with the fully solid-state approach. Unlike mechanical switches, the electronic variety tend to introduce significant voltage drops. The resistance meter circuit could be adjusted to take these voltage drops into account, but it is likely that the stability and general accuracy of the circuit would be reduced to some extend. The drawback of using relays is that it can result in a bulky and expensive finished product. However, many modern relays are now quite small and quite cheap, which makes them a practical proposition for an application such as this. The relay contacts only switch low currents at low voltages, so even a miniature relay (or a reed type) should have adequate contact ratings.

In order to provide the range switching it is necessary to use four relays (one per range). Figure 2.14 shows the circuit

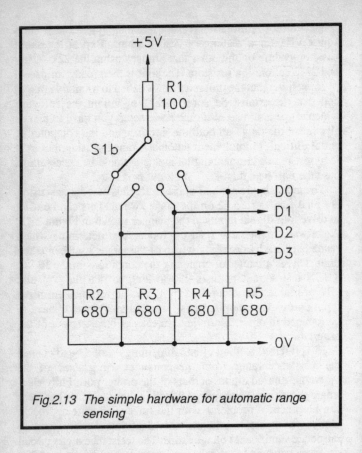

Fig.2.13 The simple hardware for automatic range
sensing

diagram for a suitable quad relay driver. The four sections are
identical, and each consists of an emitter follower switch driving the relay coil, plus a protection diode across the relay coil.
The protection diode is needed to suppress the high reverse
voltage generated across the coil when it is switched off.
Although this signal is at a fairly high impedance, semiconductor devices are very vulnerable to excessive voltages,
and the driver transistors could easily be damaged if the diodes
were omitted. The diodes clip the voltage spikes at a safe level
of about –0.7 volts.

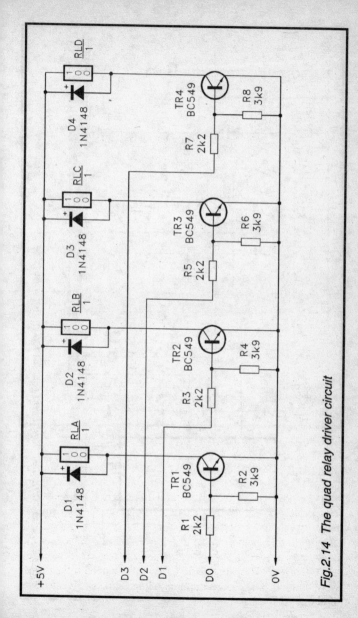

Fig.2.14 The quad relay driver circuit

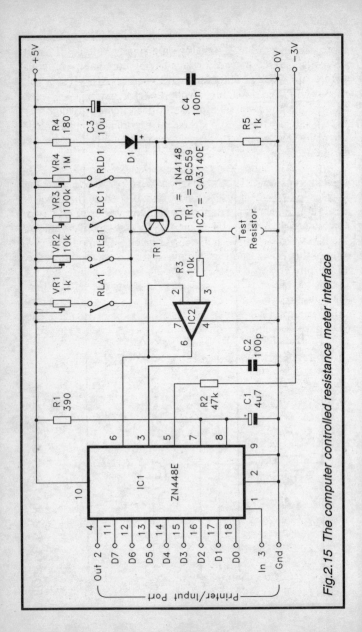

Fig.2.15 The computer controlled resistance meter interface

102

The relays must have a coil resistance of about 100 ohms or more, and must operate reliably on a supply voltage of about 4.7 volts. I found that reed relays having nominal 5 volt coils with a resistance of 500 ohms gave good results. Most 6 volt relays will operate reliably at voltages down to about 4.5 volts, and are therefore suitable for use in this circuit provided they have a suitably high coil resistance. Unfortunately, many modern 6 volt relays have coil resistances of about 50 ohms, and are unsuitable.

Figure 2.15 shows the relay controlled version of the resistance meter circuit. This is reliant on the software activating the correct relay, and only that relay, which is something that is easily implemented in practice. Outputting values of one, two, four, and eight to the printer port data lines respectively selects the 2.55k, 25.5k, 255k, and 2.55M ranges. This modified version of the resistance meter circuit writes the appropriate value to the printer port data lines when the range is changed. This operates in the same basic way as the original circuit, but there are additional IF . . . THEN instructions which write the appropriate values to the printer port data lines. The resistance meter is initially set to range one (zero to 2.55k) by lines 30 to 45.

```
10   REM RANGE SELECTING RESISTANCE METER PROGRAM
20   CLS
30   Y = 100
40   B$ = "k"
50   OUT &H378,1
60   OUT &H37A,4
70   OUT &H37A,0
80   OUT &H37A,4
90   OUT &H37A,5
100  LSN = INP(&H379) AND 240
110  LSN = LSN/16
120  OUT &H37A,4
130  MSN = INP(&H379) AND 240
140  BYTE = LSN + MSN
150  A$ = INKEY$
160  IF LEN(A$) = 1 THEN GOSUB 230
170  CLS
```

```
180   IF BYTE = 255 THEN PRINT "POSSIBLE OVERLOAD!"
190   PRINT BYTE/Y B$
200   FOR DELAY = 1 TO 10000
210   NEXT DELAY
220   GOTO 60
230   IF ASC(A$) = 49 THEN Y = 100
240   IF ASC(A$) = 49 THEN B$ = "k"
250   IF ASC(A$) = 49 THEN OUT &H378,1
260   IF ASC(A$) = 50 THEN Y = 10
270   IF ASC(A$) = 50 THEN B$ = "k"
280   IF ASC(A$) = 50 THEN OUT &H378,2
290   IF ASC(A$) = 51 THEN Y = 1
300   IF ASC(A$) = 51 THEN B$ = "k"
310   IF ASC(A$) = 51 THEN OUT &H378,4
320   IF ASC(A$) = 52 THEN Y = 100
330   IF ASC(A$) = 52 THEN B$ = "M"
340   IF ASC(A$) = 52 THEN OUT &H378,8
350   IF ASC(A$) = 53 THEN END
360   RETURN
```

Components for Resistance Meter (Figure 2.12)

Resistors (all 0.25 watt 5% carbon film)

R1	390R
R2	47k
R3	10k
R4	180R
R5	1k

Potentiometers

VR1	1k min preset
VR2	10k min preset
VR3	100k min preset
VR4	1M min preset

Capacitors

C1	4µ7 63V elect
C2	100p ceramic plate
C3	10µ 250V elect
C4	100n ceramic

Semiconductors
IC1   ZN448E
IC2   CA3140E
TR1   BC559
D1   1N4148

Miscellaneous
S1   4-way 3-pole rotary switch
             (only one pole used)
             8 pin d.i.l. holder
             14 pin d.i.l. holder
             Test sockets and leads (e.g. 1mm sockets
             and plugs plus crocodile clips)
             Case, circuit board, control knob, etc.

(Note that one of the input ports described in Chapter 1 is also
required.)

Capacitance Measurement

Capacitance measurement is slightly more difficult than
resistance measurement, but it can still be reasonably simple
provided neither very high nor extremely low values must be
measured. There is more than one method of providing capacitance measurement, but the most simple is to use a clock
oscillator driving a monostable multivibrator (Figure 2.16).
The latter provides output pulses of a duration that is inde-
pendent of the trigger signal from the clock oscillator. The
pulse length is governed by the time constant of a simple $C - R$
network. The capacitive element of this network is the capacitor under test.

The output from the monostable is therefore a series of pulses at a constant rate which is determined by the clock generator. The width of the pulses is governed by the test capacitance,
and is proportional to the capacitance. If a test capacitor gave
the output waveform of Figure 2.17(a), then one of double that
value would give the waveform of Figure 2.17(b), and one four
times that value would give the waveform of Figure 2.17(c).
The point to note here is that the average voltage in the waveform of Figure 2.17(b) is double that of Figure 2.17(a), while

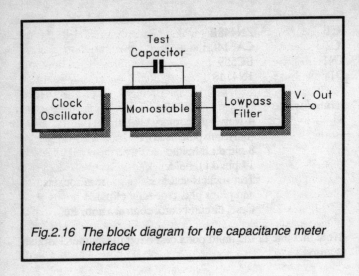

Fig.2.16 The block diagram for the capacitance meter interface

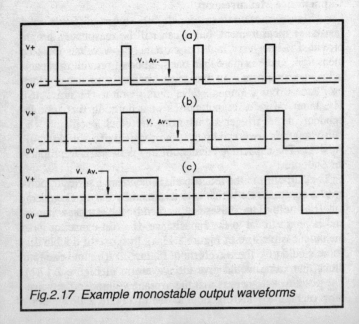

Fig.2.17 Example monostable output waveforms

that in Figure 2.17(c) is double that of Figure 2.17(b). In other words, the average output voltage is proportional to the test capacitance. Converting the pulsed waveform into a corresponding average d.c. voltage merely requires the addition of a simple lowpass filter circuit at the output of the monostable.

If the clock frequency and the timing resistance are chosen correctly, the output voltage will have a relationship that makes it easy to convert readings from the converter into the corresponding capacitance values. For example, if things are arranged so that an output of one volt per nanofarad is produced, dividing values by one hundred will give readings in nanofarads, or multiplying by ten will give readings in picofarads.

Figures 2.18 and 2.19 show the circuit diagram for a capacitance meter interface based on a ZN448E series converter. This is another circuit "borrowed" from "Electronic Projects For Your PC", incidentally. The clock oscillator uses IC1 in the standard 555 astable (oscillator) mode. VR1 enables some variation in the operating frequency, and this is needed for calibration purposes. The monostable is based on IC2, which is another 555 timer. This type of monostable can only provide output pulses that are longer than the input pulses – not shorter. This is potentially a fatal flaw in the current context, but this problem is overcome by using a clock oscillator circuit that generates very short negative output pulses. This is achieved by giving R2 a value which is low in comparison to the series resistance of R1 and VR1, so that C2's discharge time is kept very short.

A low power version of the 555 is specified for IC1 and IC2, and there are two reasons for this. One is that the minimum pulse duration from a low power 555 is shorter than that from a standard 555. This avoids problems with poor accuracy at low readings due to d.c. offsets on the output voltage. The other is that a low power 555 seems to have less than half the self-capacitance of an ordinary 555, which gives better accuracy when measuring small capacitances. Although the TS555CN is specified for IC1 and IC2, the ICM7555 and other low power 555 timers should also give satisfactory results.

IC2 has four switched timing resistors, giving four measuring ranges. R6 to R3 respectively give full scale values of

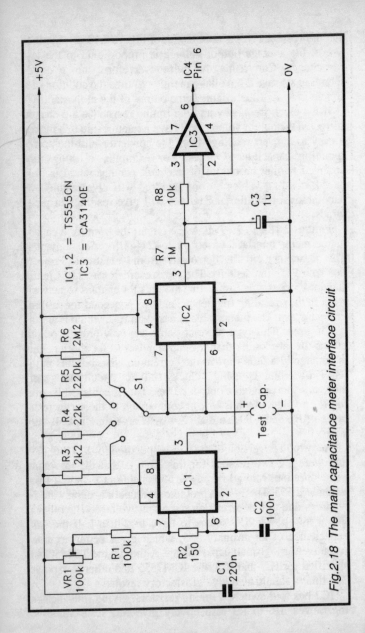

Fig.2.18 The main capacitance meter interface circuit

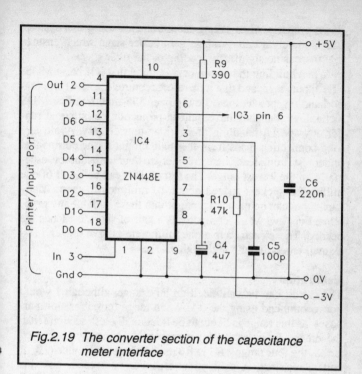

Fig.2.19 The converter section of the capacitance
meter interface

2.55n, 25.5n, 255n, and 2.55μ. A timing resistor value of 220
ohms would give a further range of 0 to 25.5μ, but would give
a relatively high current through the timing network. I noticed
no ill effects when I tried this on the prototype interface, but I
can not guarantee that it will give satisfactory results in every
case. Note that it is perfectly all right to test electrolytics or
other polarised capacitors with this equipment, but they must
be connected to the test sockets with the polarity shown in
Figure 2.18.

The filter at the output of the monostable is a simple single
stage C – R type. The long time constant of one second gives a
well smoothed d.c. output voltage, but it results in a slight delay
before the circuit adjusts to a change in test capacitance and
displays an accurate reading. Always wait for readings to settle

down properly when taking measurements using this system. IC3 is merely a unity voltage gain buffer stage which ensures that there is no significant loading of the filter stage.

When building the circuit bear in mind that IC1 has a MOS-FET input stage, and that it therefore requires the usual anti-static handling precautions. Low power 555 timers utilize MOS technology, but they have built-in protection circuits that render any special handling precautions unnecessary. Avoid any long connecting leads from the main circuit to the component under test. Long leads here are likely to degrade accuracy, especially on the lowest range. The test sockets can be a pair of one millimetre sockets spaced about 10 millimetres apart. Many capacitors can be plugged straight into these without any problems. For "awkward" components a pair of short test leads are needed. These each have a one millimetre plug at one end and a small crocodile clip at the other.

Calibration

The circuit can be calibrated on any range, although I would not recommend using the 0 to 2.55n range for calibration purposes, as this range is likely to be fractionally less accurate than the others. In order to obtain reasonably consistent accuracy across the four ranges, R3 to R6 must be close tolerance (1% or better) resistors. A calibration capacitor is needed, and this should have a value which is equal to something approaching the full scale value of the range on which the unit is to be calibrated.

For this example we will assume that the unit is to be calibrated on the 0 to 25.5n range, and that a 22n calibration component is to be used. Set S1 to the appropriate range, set VR1 at a roughly mid setting, and then connect the calibration capacitor across the input sockets. VR1 is then adjusted for a reading of 22.0n. It can be a little tricky to get the adjustment spot-on due to a slight sluggishness in the unit to respond to changes in VR1's setting. This is due to the long time constant of the filter stage. However, if VR1 is adjusted slowly and carefully it is not too difficult to find the correct setting.

It must be pointed out that a capacitor which has an excessive value for the range in use can actually provide an in-range reading. What happens here is that the output pulses from IC1 become very long, so that the monostable only triggers on (say) every other clock cycle. This can result in an output voltage as low as half the supply voltage, or 2.5 volts in this case. Clearly this is within the 2.55 volt full range potential of the converter. The easiest way of avoiding erroneous results is to have values above 240 produce an overload warning. An input voltage to the converter of under 2.4 volts is then needed to give an in-range reading. This can not occur with a capacitor that has an excessive reading even if the actual supply voltage is fractionally lower than the nominal 5 volt level.

This GW BASIC listing is for use with the capacitance meter interface, and it follows along much the same basic lines as the resistance meter program.

```
10   REM CAPACITANCE METER PROGRAM
20   CLS
30   Y = 100
40   B$ = "n"
50   OUT &H37A,4
60   OUT &H37A,0
70   OUT &H37A,4
80   OUT &H37A,5
90   LSN = INP(&H379) AND 240
100  LSN = LSN/16
110  OUT &H37A,4
120  MSN = INP(&H379) AND 240
130  BYTE = LSN + MSN
140  A$ = INKEY$
150  IF LEN(A$) = 1 THEN GOSUB 220
160  CLS
170  IF BYTE > 240 THEN PRINT "POSSIBLE OVERLOAD!"
180  PRINT BYTE/Y B$
190  FOR DELAY = 1 TO 10000
200  NEXT DELAY
210  GOTO 50
220  IF ASC(A$) = 49 THEN Y = 100
230  IF ASC(A$) = 49 THEN B$ = "n"
240  IF ASC(A$) = 50 THEN Y = 10
250  IF ASC(A$) = 50 THEN B$ = "n"
260  IF ASC(A$) = 51 THEN Y = 1
```

```
270  IF ASC(A$) = 51 THEN B$ = "n"
280  IF ASC(A$) = 52 THEN Y = 100
290  IF ASC(A$) = 52 THEN B$ = "u"
300  IF ASC(A$) = 53 THEN END
310  RETURN
```

Components for Capacitance Meter (Figures 2.18 and 2.19)

Resistors

R1	100k 5% carbon film
R2	150R 5% carbon film
R3	2k2 1% metal film
R4	22k 1% metal film
R5	220k 1% metal film
R6	2M2 1% metal film
R7	1M 5% carbon film
R8	10k 5% carbon film
R9	390R 5% carbon film
R10	47k 5% carbon film

Potentiometer

VR1	100k preset

Capacitors

C1	220n ceramic
C2	100n polyester
C3	1µ 63V elect
C4	4µ7 63V elect
C5	100p ceramic plate
C6	220n ceramic

Semiconductors

IC1	TS555CN (see text)
IC2	TS555CN (see text)
IC3	CA3140E
IC4	ZN448E

Miscellaneous

S1	4-way 3-pole rotary switch (only one pole used)

8 pin d.i.l. holder (3 off)
14 pin d.i.l. holder
Test sockets and leads (e.g. 1mm sockets
and plugs plus crocodile clips)
Case, circuit board, control knob, etc.

(Note that one of the input ports described in Chapter 1 is also required.)

Of course, if desired the range switching of the capacitance meter interface can be controlled from the computer using the same arrangement that was suggested for the resistance meter interface. The method of automatic range sensing described previously is also applicable to this project.

Biofeedback

The subject of biofeedback is by no means a new one, but it seems to have become quite topical in recent years. Stress in the modern world seems to be an ever increasing problem, and this has resulted in a lot of interest in practically every means of stress reduction. There is particular interest in methods such as biofeedback, which offer a method of stress reduction that does not involve drugs which could be addictive, or have other undesirable long-term effects.

The basic idea is to have some form of electronic monitoring device that indicates to the user how stressed or relaxed they are. The user tries to relax, and the electronic monitor indicates how well (or otherwise) they fare. If something the user does proves to be beneficial and produces greater relaxation, they try to do that some more. If something the user does produces greater stress, they try to avoid doing it again. In this way it is possible for most people to reduce their stress levels. The user effectively forms part of a negative feedback loop that controls his or her stress level. It is presumably from this that the biofeedback name is derived. Biofeedback is a method some find more effective than others, but practically anyone should be able to obtain some benefit from it.

There are various ways of monitoring the degree of stress in the human body. Some systems operate by monitoring the user's heart rate. In general, the more relaxed someone becomes, the lower their heart rate; and the more stressed they become, the higher their heart rate. The user therefore tries to obtain the lowest reading from the monitor. Another method is to monitor skin temperature. Circulation tends to be better when we are relaxed, and worse when we are stressed. This is reflected in higher and lower skin temperatures (respectively), particularly at the body's extremities such as the fingers and toes. The user therefore attempts to obtain the highest possible reading with this method.

Another simple but effective method, and the one utilized here, is to monitor the user's skin resistance. The resistance between any two patches of skin, even if they are quite close together, is normally quite high. Stress causes increased perspiration, which results in a significant reduction in skin resistance. In absolute terms the resistance is still likely to be quite high. The exact figure is dependent on a number of factors, including the size of the electrodes, the distance between them, and the thickness of the subject's skin. Typically there would be a resistance of about one megohm when the subject is relaxed, and a few hundred kilohms when they are severely stressed. Some areas of the body produce a greater degree of change than others. The hands are a good area to monitor, and most people get sweaty fingertips and palms when they are nervous or stressed.

The ZN448E analogue input port could be used as the basis of a skin resistance stress monitor, but in a simple application of this type an analogue input of the joystick port offers a simpler alternative. In this application we are not interested in accurately measuring skin resistance, and only require a relative indication. The non-linearity of the analogue converter and the opto-coupler is therefore of no great significance in this case.

On the face of it, skin resistance could be monitored by simply connecting the two electrodes across a +5 volt output and an analogue input of the joystick port. In practice this would be unlikely to work well because it would be difficult to get a low enough resistance across the electrodes. As pointed out in Chapter 1, the joystick port's analogue inputs cover a range of zero to about 150k or so. In this application the resistance being monitored will usually be more than 150k, and in some case will be more than ten times this figure.

114

Even if this method did provide in-range readings, it would still be an unsatisfactory way of doing things. Most PCs are mains powered, and this makes it essential to have an isolated coupling from the user to the input port of the PC. The electrodes are taped in place, and this would make it difficult for the user to detach him or herself from the electrodes if a fault resulted in an electric shock being received. In order to conform to the safety regulations there must be an isolated link between the user and the computer. In the event of the computer succumbing to a power supply fault, the isolated link should prevent the user from receiving any electric shock at all.

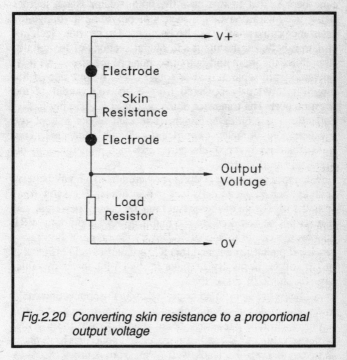

Fig.2.20 Converting skin resistance to a proportional output voltage

The obvious way of handling things is to use the electrodes in a potential divider connected across the supply rails, as shown in Figure 2.20. The lower the user's skin resistance, the higher the output voltage from the potential divider.

Connecting the output of the potential divider to the input of the voltage-to-resistance converter circuit described in Chapter 1 (Figure 1.29) enables the user to monitor their skin resistance. Lower readings then indicate increased relaxation, and higher readings indicate a more stressful state. The user must therefore try to obtain the lowest possible reading.

The Circuit
Figure 2.21 shows the circuit diagram for the biofeedback interface, which has obvious similarities with the basic voltage-to-resistance converter of Figure 1.29. An important point to note here is that in this case the opto-isolator is not merely being used as a convenient means of providing a voltage-to-resistance conversion. It is also being used to provide electrical isolation between the input and output sections of the circuit. Therefore, the input and output sections of the circuit must be powered from separate power sources. The output side of the circuit is obviously powered from a +5 volt output of the joystick port. The transistor at the output of IC2 simply has its collector and emitter terminals connected where one of the joystick potentiometers would normally be connected. This transistor does not provide pure resistance, but this is of no practical significance.

The input side of the circuit is powered from a 6 volt battery, such as four HP7 size cells in a plastic holder. For safety reasons the input side of the circuit must be battery powered, and it must not be powered from a mains power supply unit. VR1 enables the circuit to accommodate a wide range of skin resistances. If the electrodes and (or) IC2 are particularly efficient it might still be necessary to make R1 and VR1 lower in value, say 10k and 220k respectively.

C2 helps to filter out noise picked up in the connecting cable to the electrodes. If noise pick up still proves to be a problem, with very "jittery" readings being returned from the joystick port, the value of C2 can be increased to about 1μ. However, it is better to keep the leads well away from sources of mains "hum", such as mains leads, so that the amount of stray pick up is kept to a low level, rather than trying to filter out a large amount of noise.

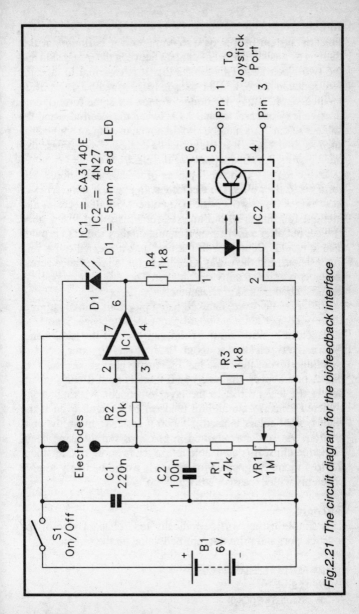

Fig.2.21 The circuit diagram for the biofeedback interface

IC1 = CA3140E
IC2 = 4N27
D1 = 5mm Red LED

To Joystick Port
Pin 1
Pin 3

D1
6
7
2
3
4
IC1

R4 1k8
IC2
5
6
4

R3 1k8

Electrodes

C1 220n
R2 10k
C2 100n
R1 47k
VR1 1M

S1 On/Off
B1 6V

117

In Use

For any system of this type to work well it is important that there is a consistent level of contact between the user's skin and the two electrodes. This means that it is essential to tape the electrodes in place, and the user must keep reasonably still. In medical applications it is quite common for some form of conductive jelly or paste to be used between the electrodes and the subject's skin. This method should not be used in an application such as this, where it is the subject's degree of sweatiness that must govern the effectiveness of the electrodes.

In theory, any two small pieces of clean metal should perform perfectly well as the electrodes. In practice some types of electrode seem to work better than others. Small pieces of aluminium foil about 20 millimetres square seemed like a good choice, but after a lot of experimentation they failed to provide usable results. Contact with the user's skin seemed to be very inconsistent, and there was a tendency for the resistance across the electrodes to steadily drift higher. This effect swamped any genuine change in skin resistance.

Better results were obtained using pieces of thin aluminium sheet or copper laminate board about the same size. These can be taped in position on the palm and back of the same hand. Alternatively, electrodes about 10 by 20 millimetres taped to two fingertips of the same hand seems to give good results. In the case of copper laminate board there is no difficulty in soldering the leads direct to the layer of copper. Making strong soldered joints to aluminium tends to be difficult even if the right type of solder is used. I found it easier to make the connections via soldertags bolted in place, or simply using small crocodile clips. It is advisable to use leads no more than about 0.5 to 1 metre long, since longer leads would be likely to give problems with excessive stray pick up.

Software

This simple listing will periodically read channel zero of the joystick port and print the returned value on the screen.

```
10   REM BIOFEEDBACK PROGRAM
20   CLS
30   SKINRES = STICK(0)
```

```
40    PRINT SKINRES
50    A$ = INKEY$
60    IF LEN(A$) = 1 THEN END
70    FOR DELAY = 1 TO 20000
80    NEXT DELAY
90    CLS
100   GOTO 30
```

Line 30 reads the channel 0 analogue input and places the reading in variable "SKINRES". This value is then printed on the screen at line 40. The next two lines check to see if the keyboard has been operated, and bring the program to a halt if a key has been depressed. Therefore, pressing any character key will break out of the program and bring things to a halt. After a delay at lines 70 and 80 the screen is cleared, and the program is looped back to line 30 where a fresh reading is taken. In use do not expect very rapid changes in readings. A sudden increase in stress might actually produce quite a rapid response from the system, but changes in the opposite direction will generally be quite slow and gradual. Remember that the idea is to achieve the lowest possible reading.

A computer based system can go beyond simply printing values on the screen. The computer can be used to provide feedback in a form that will aid relaxation. The obvious way of doing this is to use computer graphics, changes in screen colour, effects from the sound generator, etc., to produce pleasing effects as the values returned from the joystick port gradually reduce. Relatively complex programming of this type goes well beyond the scope of this hardware oriented book, but it is possible that those who have the necessary programming skills might like to explore.

Temperature Monitor
When using the analogue inputs of the joystick port the sensor may provide a resistance range that is a good match for the port. Except where safety considerations dictate otherwise, the sensor can then be connected direct to the joystick port. Where the resistance range is not suitable it is necessary to resort to a circuit of the type used for the biofeedback interface (Figure

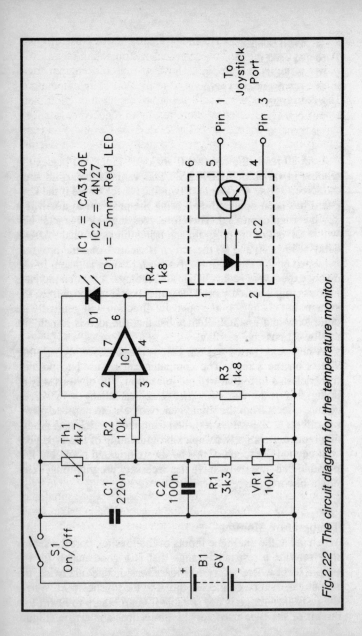

Fig.2.22 The circuit diagram for the temperature monitor.

IC1 = CA3140E
IC2 = 4N27
D1 = 5mm Red LED

120

2.21), using values for R1 and VR1 that return a useful range of values from the port over the sensor's operating range.

For example, Figure 2.22 shows the circuit diagram for a simple interface that can be used to monitor skin temperature. The thermistor is a standard negative temperature coefficient type (i.e. increased temperature results in reduced resistance), and it has a resistance of 4k7 at 25 degrees Celsius. The component used in the prototype is actually a Maplin miniature bead type thermistor, but the circuit should work just as well using any similar thermistor. Skin temperature is normally a little higher than 25 degrees, giving a typical operating resistance through Th1 of about 4k. If connected direct to an analogue input on the joystick port this resistance would barely register, and small changes in temperature would not give any change in the reading obtained.

Using the voltage-to-resistance converter circuit it is possible to use a load resistance that provides typical values from the port that are somewhere near the middle of the range. In other words, VR1 is adjusted so that initially values of about 75 to 80 are read from the joystick port. This gives much improved scaling, and small temperature changes will produce variations in the readings from the port, giving much more useful results.

The temperature interface can be used with the skin resistance biofeedback program. In this case the user is trying to produce the highest possible skin temperature, which means they must try to produce the highest possible reading from the interface. This is the opposite way round to the skin resistance monitor. Simply swap-over the two arms of the potential divider if you would prefer things the other way round. Of course, with four analogue inputs on the joystick port it is quite possible to monitor skin resistance and temperature simultaneously. In fact it would be possible to accommodate skin resistance and temperature monitoring for two people at once.

Digital Inputs

Digital input ports are often used in rather low-tech ways, such as monitoring micro-switches, keyboard switches, and the like. In this section we will consider various ways of using digital inputs to monitor simple switches, as well as some slightly

121

higher-tech sensors such as optical types. We will start with some simple methods of position sensing for use in model railway applications, robotics, etc.

When controlling model trains, robot arms, and so on, it is often necessary to have some form of feedback from the device being controlled if proper automatic control is to be achieved. For example, it is quite easy to have a model train controller that is computer controlled, with the train stopping and starting without the need for any human intervention. However, in its most basic form this results in the train stopping and starting at random positions on the track. The results obtained do not really justify the effect involved. With the aid of a simple feedback mechanism the train can be made to stop and start at any desired point (or points) on the track, giving much more pleasing results.

In general, the more sophisticated the feedback to the controller, the greater the accuracy that can be achieved in any control application. In our model train example, a single sensor could detect the train some way ahead of the station. The train could then be automatically decelerated and made to stop at the station. The problem with this type of thing is in getting consistent results, with the train always stopping exactly at the right place. Provided the train was always travelling at the same speed as it passed the sensor, with some trial and error it would probably be possible to get the train to stop in more or less the same place each time. This simple setup might provide adequate accuracy, or it might not. The only way to find out would be to try it in practice. In my experience a simple setup of this type usually falls just short of providing acceptable results.

If the train was not always travelling at the same speed as it passed the sensor (which is likely to be the case in practice), the chances of success would be very small. In theory it would be possible to have a suitable deceleration rate precalculated for each possible speed, but in practice the chances of implementing such a system successfully are remote. The time involved in getting everything just right would be enormous, and the degree of accuracy obtained would fall some way short of being acceptable.

A better way of handling things is to have two sensors. As before, one would be some way ahead of the station, and on passing this one the train would be made to decelerate. However, it would not be brought to a complete halt. Instead, after the deceleration phase the train would be made to keep moving very slowly. The second sensor would be positioned in the station, and the train would be brought to a halt as it passed this sensor. In this way very precise positioning of the train can be achieved. Furthermore, it can be achieved very easily, which makes the addition of the second sensor very worthwhile indeed.

Further sensors could be added ahead of the station so that the deceleration of the train could be controlled very accurately, and greater realism could be achieved. This is something where the laws of diminishing returns come into play though. Adding one sensor gives a tremendous improvement to the system. Adding a second one also brings great benefits, making it much easier to obtain an adequate degree of accuracy, as well as giving much greater realism. Adding further sensors does permit improved results to be obtained, but the improvement is less obvious. With each sensor that is added, the improvement it provides is that much less than that provided by its predecessor. Whether or not it is worth using more than two sensors really depends on how much of a perfectionist you happen to be.

Reed Switches
A micro-switch is the simplest and most convenient form of sensor for robotics and some other applications. A micro-switch is basically just an ordinary switch, but instead of having manual operation via a push-button, slider knob, or whatever, it has some sort of lever mechanism that is operated automatically. For example, a micro-switch could be positioned such that it is operated when a robot arm is moved round to a certain position. A micro-switch can be used as a model train sensor if the lever can be positioned where it will be activated by the passing train. In practice it is often difficult to obtain reliable results using this method, and if you get things slightly wrong there can be frequent derailments!

A reed switch is a more popular method of sensing for model train applications. A reed switch is basically just two small pieces of springy metal that overlap one another, as in Figure

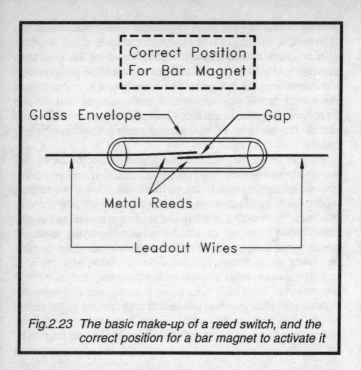

Fig.2.23 *The basic make-up of a reed switch, and the correct position for a bar magnet to activate it*

2.23. These pieces of metal are the "reeds", and they are normally fitted in a glass envelope. The reeds are spaced slightly apart so that they are not quite in electrical contact with each other. If you look carefully at one of these switches you should be able to see the reeds and the gap through the glass casing.

If a reasonably strong bar magnet is placed next to a reed switch, the two reeds become temporarily magnetised by the field of the magnet. The two ends of the reeds that are in close proximity to each other have opposite poles, and accordingly they are attracted to one another. Due to the flexible nature of the reeds, this results in the overlapping ends moving together and touching, so that electrical contact is completed. This gives a simple switching action, with the switch open when the magnet is absent, and closed when it is brought close to the reeds. The contact ratings of reed switches are very low incidentally, but they are more than adequate for position sensing, where they will typically handle only about 5 to 10 milliamps at 5 to 12 volts d.c.

The magnet must normally be within about 20 to 30 millimetres of the reed switch before the latter will be activated. Although this gives a very short operating range, it is sufficient for use in computerised model train systems, and many other computer control applications. An important factor in favour of this system for model train use is that there is no need for any direct contact between the train and the sensor. This totally avoids any problems with the sensors causing derailments.

Positioning of the bar magnet is crucial, and the reed switch will simply not operate if the relative orientation of the magnet is not correct. The magnet must be parallel to the switch, as shown in Figure 2.23. Having the magnet perpendicular to the reeds will not close the switch even at point-blank range. In model train applications the reed switch is often placed under the track, and the magnet is fitted in the base of a piece of rolling stock. If the reed switch is fitted across the track, then the magnet must be fitted across the carriage or truck. My preference is to have the reed switch running along the middle of the track. The magnet must then be fitted lengthwise along the base section of the piece of rolling stock, and not across it.

Figure 2.24 shows the two basic methods of using a reed switch (or any other mechanical switch) to drive a digital input of a computer. The difference between the two is that the output of (a) is normally low and goes high when the switch is activated, while the output of (b) is normally high and goes low when the switch is activated. In a computer application it does not normally matter which method of connection is used, as the software can be written to suit either method. My preference is for the method shown in (a), as it is easier to think in terms of a returned value of 0 as the standby state, and a returned value of one, two, etc., as the active state.

Although this type of sensor may seem to be so simple that nothing could go wrong in practice, there are a few potential problems. Mechanical switches are notoriously noisy, and often suffer from a certain amount of contact bounce. This results in a series of brief pulses being produced each time the switch opens or closes, rather than single "clean" transitions being produced.

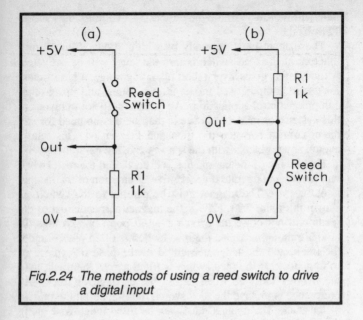

Fig.2.24 *The methods of using a reed switch to drive a digital input*

The importance of this (or the lack of it) depends on whether or not the switch circuit feeds into an edge triggered input. If it does, there is a real danger of multiple triggering occurring. There are software solutions, the most simple of which is to have a time delay so that once a trigger signal has been detected, no others are serviced for a short period of time. Hardware solutions are more popular though, and are extremely simple. The basic technique is to use a pulse stretcher which holds the output in the active state for a short while once an initial trigger pulse has been received.

This technique can also be of benefit if the switch circuit is used to drive an ordinary (non-edge triggered) digital input. If only momentary operation of the switch will be produced (such as in a model train position sensor), it is possible that the routine which monitors the input port will sometimes miss the input pulses. The likelihood of this depends on how frequently the monitoring routine will test the input lines, but using a pulse stretcher to give pulses of (say) about one second in duration should ensure that there is absolute no possibility of any pulses being missed.

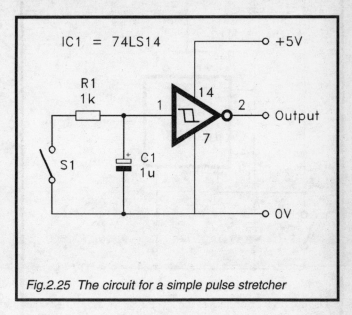

Fig.2.25 The circuit for a simple pulse stretcher

Figure 2.25 shows the circuit diagram for a very simple pulse stretcher based on a trigger/inverter stage. The latter is one of the six trigger/inverters in a 74LS14. This does not provide a particularly long output pulse, but it is usually sufficient to provide effective de-bouncing. It is very economic since six resistors, six capacitors, and one 74LS14 will provide half a dozen de-bounce circuits.

For a longer output pulse duration the basic 555 monostable circuit of Figure 2.26 can be used. R2 and C1 are the timing components, and the pulse duration is equal to 1.1 C R seconds (where C is the timing capacitor value in microfarads, and R is the timing resistance in megohms). The specified values give a pulse duration of about 1.1 seconds, but using larger timing component values it is possible to obtain pulse durations of several seconds if necessary.

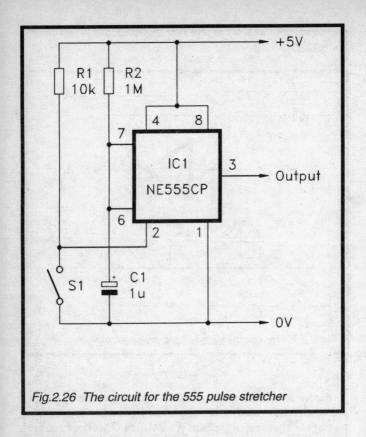

Fig.2.26 The circuit for the 555 pulse stretcher

Opto Sensor

If you would prefer to use a more modern method of sensing, an optical sensor is a good choice. The circuit of Figure 2.27 is based on a reflective opto-sensor, which is basically just an infra-red l.e.d. and a photo-transistor in the same case, and "looking" in the same direction. The sensor I used is the RS "standard" type (the type number given in Figure 2.27 is actually the RS/Electromail order code, with no type number being given for this device in the catalogues). Figure 2.28 provides connection details for this device. The circuit will also work with the RS "miniature" reflective opto-sensor, or the Maplin OPB706B (which seems to be identical to the RS "miniature"

128

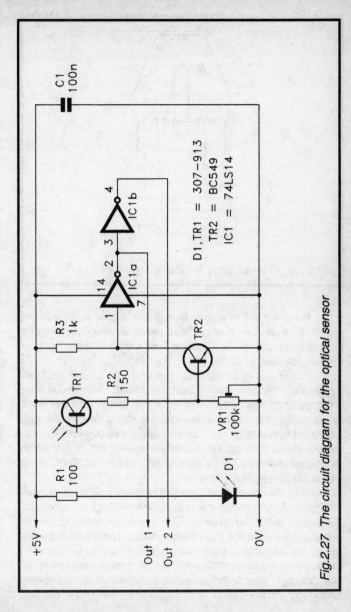

C1
100n

4
IC1b

3

14 2
IC1a
7   1

D1,TR1 = 307–913
TR2   = BC549
IC1   = 74LS14

R3
1k

TR2

TR1

R2
150

VR1
100k

R1
100

D1

+5V

Out 1
Out 2

0V

Fig.2.27 The circuit diagram for the optical sensor

129

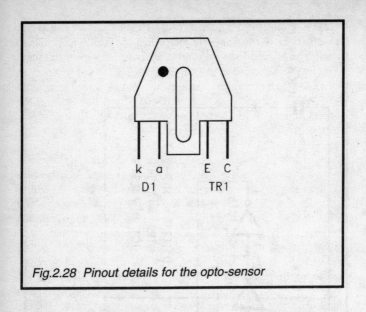

Fig.2.28 Pinout details for the opto-sensor

type). However, the miniature type seems to give slightly lower sensitivity than the "standard" size sensor. It would presumably be possible to improvise a sensor from a separate phototransistor and infra-red LED but I have not tried this.

The basic idea of a reflective opto-sensor is to have the l.e.d. transmit a constant beam of infra-red "light". The photo-transistor picks up any of the infra-red signal that is reflected back to the sensor. The l.e.d. section of the sensor is simply fed with a forward bias current via current limiting resistor R1. The latter sets the l.e.d. current at 30 milliamps, which is high enough to give good results, but is comfortably within the 50 milliamp maximum rating of the l.e.d.

Even if the object to be detected is fairly reflective, it must be very close to the sensor in order to give enough infra-red signal on the photo-transistor to fully turn it on. Much improved range can be obtained if, as in this circuit, the photo-transistor drives an amplifier stage. The amplifier is a basic common emitter switch based on TR2. VR1 permits the sensitivity of the circuit to be controlled (maximum resistance giving maximum sensitivity).

The output from TR2 may not always switch cleanly and rapidly from one logic level to the other. In fact the voltage here can hover at illegal voltages between the valid logic 0 and logic 1 potentials. Therefore, the output from TR2 is fed to a couple of Schmitt trigger/inverter stages that will always give valid logic levels, apart from fast transitions from one state to the other. Output 1 is normally low and it goes high when an object is sensed. Output 2 is an inversion of this.

Note that Figure 2.27 correctly shows no connection to the base of TR1. In fact the base terminal of TR1 is not externally accessible, and it is therefore impossible to make a connection to it. If a long lead of more than about half a metre is used to connect the reflective sensor and the main circuit, I would recommend using a multi-way screened cable. The cathode terminal of D1 should connect to the screen of the cable.

A certain amount of thought needs to be used when setting up a sensor of this type. The object to be sensed must obviously be reasonably reflective, but most things seem to reflect rather more infra-red than you would expect. Accordingly, this will not usually be a problem. However, where necessary the object to be sensed must be fitted with something that will provide the sensor with a suitably reflective target. For example, in a model train application the reflective sensor could be mounted under the track, and a small patch of aluminium foil somewhere on the underside of the train could be used as the "target" for the sensor.

This type of sensor can only operate if the normal background level of reflection is quite low. It might actually be possible to get the sensor to operate properly if there is a high level of reflection under standby conditions. It would then be a matter of setting things up so that the object to be sensed produced a reduction in the amount of reflected infra-red. It is certainly possible to do this under the right circumstances, but the normal method of operation is likely to provide better reliability, and is the one that should be used wherever possible.

It is essential to give VR1 a suitable setting if the sensor is to function reliably. This just means adjusting VR1 for highest resistance that does not result in the circuit being activated under standby conditions. An advantage of an optical sensor of this type over a reed switch is that it can provide a much greater range. Critical adjustment of VR1 may well provide an operating range of half a metre or more. In the interest of good reliability though, it is probably best to settle for an operating range of about 100 millimetres or less if the objects to be sensed are fairly small.

A drawback of this type of sensor in a model train context is that the passing train may well produce hundreds of output pulses from the sensor over a period of several seconds. A long pulse stretcher circuit could be used to combat this problem, but in this case my preference is for a software hold-off to prevent multiple triggering on each pass of the train. Alternatively, using the aluminium foil "target" method described previously, the sensitivity of the circuit could probably be backed-off to the point where only the foil "target" was sensed, and a single output pulse was produced.

Good Effect

The Hall effect was apparently discovered by E. H. Hall in 1879, but it is only in relatively recent years that it has been exploited to any great extent in practical applications. A Hall effect sensor is a semiconductor device which detects magnetic fields. Devices of this type offer a hi-tech alternative to reed switches. Unfortunately, many Hall effect devices are quite expensive, and do not really represent a realistic alternative to simple sensors such as reed and micro switches. On the other hand, there are a few low cost types which offer an interesting and practical alternative to more traditional methods of position sensing.

In essence the Hall effect is quite straightforward, and Figure 2.29 helps to explain the way in which a Hall effect sensor functions. Figure 2.29(a) represents the device with no magnetic field applied. The sensing element is basically just a piece of silicon having electrodes placed centrally on opposite surfaces. A current is passed through the piece of silicon, from top to bottom, producing a potential gradient. At the top of the slice of silicon there is the full supply voltage, at the bottom there is zero volts, and at the electrodes there is about half the supply voltage. The output voltage is taken from the two electrodes, and under quiescent conditions they are at the same

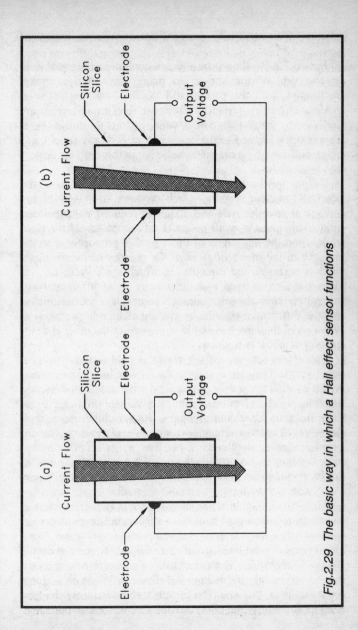

Fig.2.29 The basic way in which a Hall effect sensor functions

potential. This obviously gives a differential output voltage of zero.

Figure 2.29(b) shows the effect of applying a magnetic field to one side of the sensor. In many ways things remain unchanged, with the current still flowing, and the potential gradient still being produced. However, the current carriers are deflected by the magnetic field, which distorts the current flow. This is often likened to the beam of a cathode ray tube (c.r.t.) being deflected by a magnetic field, but in this case the deflection is much less.

Despite the limited effect of the magnetic field, it skews the potential gradient slightly, which produces a slightly higher voltage at one electrode and a slightly reduced voltage at the other. This gives a small potential difference across the electrodes, and the amplitude of this signal is proportional to the strength of the magnetic field. If the polarity of the magnetic field is reversed, the direction in which the current flow is skewed is also reversed, as is the polarity of the differential output voltage from the electrodes. Of course, it is not essential to use the differential outputs. A voltage change is produced at each output, making it possible to use one or the other if a single output signal is required.

Hall effect sensors are not normally sold in the form of a basic sensor. They are usually in the form of integrated circuits which contain the sensor plus a substantial amount of on-chip electronics. The electronics can be a simple amplifier, or an amplifier plus some control logic and a switching transistor at the output. These switching devices are the obvious choices for position sensing applications, but they either seem to be too expensive, or do not provide the right kind of switching action. An inexpensive linear device plus some discrete switching circuitry seems to be a more practical alternative.

The UGN3503U is an inexpensive linear Hall effect device, but despite its low cost it offers a very useful level of performance. It is a three lead device which looks very much like a small plastic cased transistor. Figure 2.30 shows pinout details for the UGN3503U. The encapsulation seems to be symmetrical, or very nearly so, making it difficult to decide on notional front and back surfaces. The certain method is to use the type number to identify the notional front side of the component.

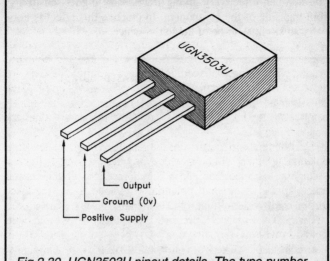

Fig.2.30 UGN3503U pinout details. The type number identifies the notional front surface

Although the UGN3503U has some built-in amplification, its sensitivity is not particularly high. It is typically about 1.3 millivolts per G. Placing the end of a bar magnet right against one surface of a UGN3503U will produce quite a large change in the output voltage (typically about one volt). At a range of about 25 millimetres the voltage change is quite low, and is typically no more than about 20 millivolts. However, this is sufficient to trigger an external switching circuit, and the device makes the good basis for a position sensor.

As one would expect, the output voltage increases for a magnetic field of one polarity, and decreases for a magnetic field of the opposite polarity. Applying a north pole to the surface that carries the type number gives a reduction in the output voltage, applying the south pole to this surface gives an increase in the output voltage (Figure 2.31). Applying the field to the opposite surface of the sensor has the opposite effect (e.g. applying a north pole gives an increase in the output potential). The sensor is positioned slightly closer to the surface which carries the

135

type number, effectively giving fractionally higher sensitivity from this side of the component. In practice this effect is normally so slight as to be of no consequence.

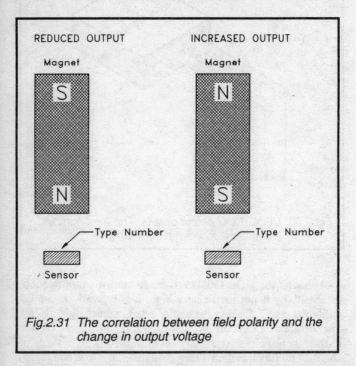

Fig.2.31 *The correlation between field polarity and the change in output voltage*

It is important to realise that the sensor will not respond to a magnetic field applied to one of the four smaller surfaces. A magnetic field from any of these directions will distort the current flow in a fashion that produces no change in the potentials at the electrodes.

Hall Switches
Figure 2.32 shows the circuit diagram for a simple position sensor based on a UGN3503U. IC1 is the Hall effect sensor, and its output voltage is at half the supply potential under standby conditions. IC2 is an operational amplifier, but it is used here as a voltage comparator. The output from IC1 is fed

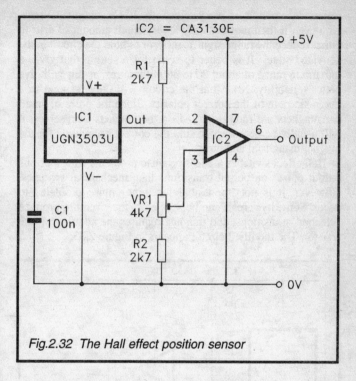

Fig.2.32 The Hall effect position sensor

to the inverting input of IC2, while R1, VR1, and R2, provide a reference potential to this input. In practice VR1 is adjusted for a reference voltage that is fractionally lower than the output voltage from IC1. With its non-inverting input at a lower voltage than its inverting input, the output of IC2 goes low. A magnetic field of the correct polarity will result in the output of IC1 going below the reference potential, and the output of IC2 then goes high. Alternatively, the reference level can be set just above the quiescent output voltage from IC1. IC2's output is then normally high. It will go to the low state if a magnetic field increases the output voltage from IC1.

I used this sensor in conjunction with a Maplin "large" bar magnet, but it should work well with any reasonably powerful bar magnet. The circuit will provide an operating range of 50 millimetres or more if VR1 is carefully adjusted so that the reference voltage is very close to IC1's output voltage. However, it then requires only a very small amount of drift to either reduce the range significantly, or to hold the circuit in the activated state. It is better to settle for a setting that gives a maximum range of about 20 to 30 millimetres, as this will give better reliability. Note that the circuit will only respond to a magnetic pole of the correct polarity. Since the poles of small bar magnets are rarely marked on the magnets themselves, it will usually be necessary to find the correct orientation for the magnet using trial and error.

Hall effect switches are less prone to problems with spurious output pulses on output transitions than mechanical switches. However, it is not impossible for minor noise problems to occur. Some hysteresis can be applied to the circuit to produce "cleaner" transitions, and this just requires the addition of one resistor. The modified circuit appears in Figure 2.33.

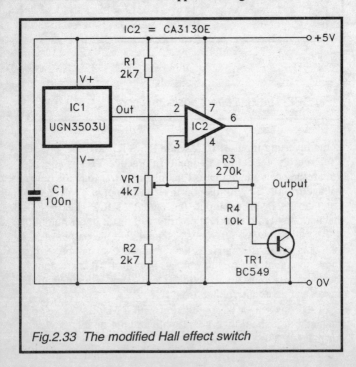

Fig.2.33 The modified Hall effect switch

R3 is the additional resistor, which provides a small amount of d.c. positive feedback over IC2. This effectively converts IC2 from a comparator to a trigger circuit. In the interest of "clean" switching it is better to use a large amount of hysteresis, which means using a relatively low value for R3. On the other hand, using a large amount of feedback reduces the sensitivity of the circuit. The value of R3 therefore has to be a compromise. The specified value should give good results, but the value of R3 can obviously be changed to suit your particular application.

The CA3130E used for IC2 works well on a 5 volt supply, and seems to drive most logic inputs without any problems. Note that most other operational amplifiers will not work properly in this circuit. The circuit might fail to drive standard TTL inputs, which could be encountered in the printer ports of older PCs. This problem can be overcome by using the open collector output stage shown in Figure 2.33. TR1 has sufficient sink current capability to pull any TTL input low. Bear in mind that TR1 provides an inversion, so its collector is low when IC2's output is high (and vice versa).

It is perhaps worth mentioning the UGN3132U Hall effect switch. This has the same encapsulation and leadout configuration as the UGN3503U, but its output is an open collector switch. Figure 2.34 shows the circuit for a simple sensor based on this device. The output load resistor is not always essential when driving logic inputs, but it is as well to include it. The UGN3132U is switched on by a magnetic field of one polarity, and switched off again by a field of the opposite polarity. This is generally less useful than a switch that is only activated while a suitable magnetic field is present, but it does have possible uses. The maximum operating range is about 20 millimetres or so with most small bar magnets.

Output Projects
Controlling electronic and electrical equipment from a computer is often quite simple and straightforward. In particular, where simple on/off switching is required, the control circuit usually consists of just a latching digital output plus about three or four components. Variable control is a little more difficult, and requires a digital to analogue converter. However, for low

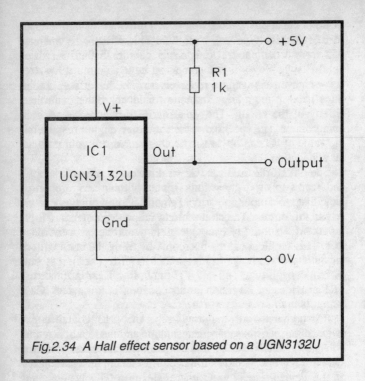

Fig.2.34 A Hall effect sensor based on a UGN3132U

voltage d.c. loads (e.g. model locomotives) the circuitry can still be kept quite simple.

A word of warning has to be given here, and this is simply that the necessary safety precautions must be taken when controlling any mains powered equipment. As explained later in this chapter, it is essential to have some form of isolation device between the computer and the controlled equipment. Without such isolation there will almost certainly be some blown fuses at switch-on, and the equipment could be very dangerous to touch. Unless you are completely sure that you understand what you are doing, you should not attempt any project which involves the control of mains powered equipment (or any project which involves making connections to the mains supply wiring).

Relay Control

A relay is just an ordinary mechanical switch that is operated via an electro-magnet. This may seem to be an out dated method of control in this computerised age, but a relay does have its advantages. One of these is simply that quite a modest input power permits massive power levels to be controlled, although I suppose that this is also true of many modern semiconductor power control devices. A relay though, provides this power control with the minimal losses associated with mechanical switches. The power loss through semiconductor power control devices is often not of great importance, but it tends to be a nuisance in that it results in a lot of heat being generated in the control device. Relays provide control of high power loads without any need to bother with heatsinking.

Probably the main advantage of relays over other methods of control is the isolation that they provide. There is no direct connection between the electro-magnet and the switch contacts. This means that, provided the normal precautions are taken, it is perfectly safe to control mains powered equipment via a relay. Obviously you must be careful to ensure that the input and output wiring to the relay are properly separated so that there is no risk of any accidental short circuits occurring here. Also, you need to carefully check the contact ratings of a relay to ensure that it can safely handle the voltage and current ratings involved in your particular application. This is something that applies whenever you use a relay, not just when it is being used in mains control applications. Note that the ratings of relay contacts are usually quite different for a.c. and d.c. loads (the d.c. ratings often being very much lower). Make sure that you check the set of ratings that are apposite to the type of power source you are using.

A simple quad relay driver circuit has already been described (Figure 2.14), and was used to provide computer controlled range switching for the resistance meter interface. This circuit was only for use with 5 volt relays, but it will work equally well with 12 volt types having a coil resistance of about 200 ohms or more (Figure 2.35). The only modifications are the change to a 12 volt relay, and the increase in supply voltage from 5 to 12 volts. Twelve volt relays are a good choice where high powers must be controlled, since there are plenty of

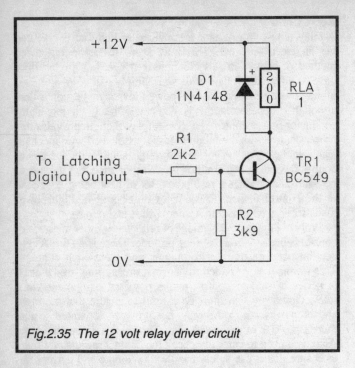

Fig.2.35 The 12 volt relay driver circuit

inexpensive relays of this type which can handle currents of around 10 amps at 240 volts a.c.

LEDs
The normal method of displaying information on a PC is, of course, via its display adapter and monitor. This is not always a good way of doing things, and is rather risky in situations where the system will be left unattended for long periods of time. Pieces of equipment such as television sets and computer monitors are considered to be a fire hazard if left unattended. Probably the best solution to the problem is to use some form of "solid state" screen, such as a liquid crystal type. However, this is likely to be a very costly solution.

A more practical solution is to opt for a simple status display of some sort. The monitor can then be switched off, with the status display then providing some basic information to show that everything is functioning correctly. At its most basic a status display just consists of a flashing LED indicator to show that everything is functioning properly. More usefully, there could be several LEDs, showing what function or functions the computer was providing at that moment. At one time it was actually quite common for large computer systems to have flashing LED displays which informed a suitably trained engineer exactly what the computer was up to. This type of thing never really seemed to catch on with microcomputers though, probably because they were used in applications where such a display was not particularly relevant. However, if you are using a microcomputer in a scientific or other technical application, a simple LED display could be extremely helpful.

In many cases it is possible to drive a LED direct from a digital output, but via a current limiting resistor of around 470 ohms in value. The only slight problem is that not all digital

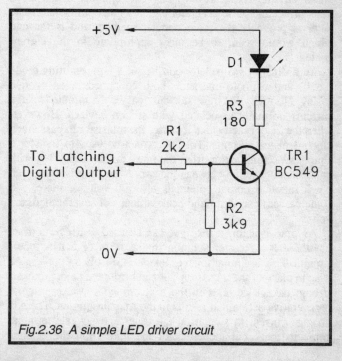

Fig.2.36 A simple LED driver circuit

outputs can provide a high enough current to give good l.e.d. brightness. Some component suppliers now offer l.e.d.s that are designed to provide good brightness when operated at low currents of around 2 milliamps, and this offers a possible solution. Another is to drive the l.e.d. via a simple common emitter driver stage, as in the circuit of Figure 2.36. R3 sets the l.e.d. current at about 20 milliamps, which should give high brightness with any modern LED.

Solid-State Control

A relay is the traditional method of controlling mains loads from electronic equipment, but there is an alternative in the form of a triac. This is a semiconductor switching device that can handle a.c. loads. The problem with using a triac is that it does not provide isolation from the mains supply, and is therefore unusable unless some form of isolation is included in the driver circuit. There are basically two options, which are a transformer and pulse generator circuit, or an opto-isolator. The latter is probably the more popular method, and is the one which would seem to be most appropriate in the current context.

An ordinary opto-isolator consists of a light emitting diode (l.e.d.) and a photo-transistor, both contained in an opaque casing. Normally the transistor only passes the minute leakage currents normally associated with silicon devices. However, when the l.e.d. is activated, it causes the transistor to pass much larger leakage currents. This effect can be used to transfer a simple switching action from the input to the output, but with no direct connection between the two. Most opto-isolators can block input to output potentials of 1500 volts or more, and some devices can withstand peak voltages of several thousand volts.

An opto-isolator of this type can be used to trigger a triac, but there is an easier solution in the form of a triac opto-isolator. This is similar to an ordinary opto-isolator, but it has a triac in place of the transistor. The light from the l.e.d. produces strong leakage currents in the triac, which cause an internal regenerative action that results in the triac turning on. There is no gate current to switch on the triac (and no gate terminal come to that), but the effect of the light from the l.e.d. is

144

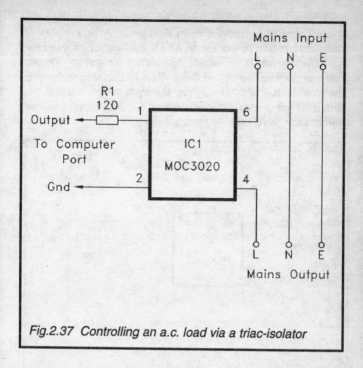

Fig.2.37 Controlling an a.c. load via a triac-isolator

effectively the same as a normal gate trigger signal.

Figure 2.37 shows the circuit diagram for a computer controlled mains switch using an MOC3020 (or similar) opto-triac isolator. On the input side R1 provides current limiting for the l.e.d. Pin 2 of IC1 is the cathode of the l.e.d., and so it is this terminal that connects to the 0 volt rail of the computer. R1 is fed from a line of the latching digital output port. On the output side the triac is used to switch the "Live" side of the mains supply. Note that there is no internal connection to pin 3 of the MOC3020. There is an internal connection to pin 5, which connects to the substrate of the triac section of the devices. No external connection should be made to this pin.

There is a major limitation to a circuit of this type in that the opto-triac isolator has a very modest current rating of just 100 milliamps. When used on the 240 volt mains supply this means that a maximum power of just 24 watts can be controlled. This is adequate for a few applications, but is obviously totally inadequate for most potential uses of the circuit. A simple way of controlling higher power loads is to use a triac isolator to control a high power triac. Figure 2.38 shows the circuit diagram for a mains switching circuit that utilizes this slaving technique. The triac in IC1 acts as a bilateral switch which triggers the main triac via current limiting resistor R2. As before, the triac switches the "live" side of the mains supply.

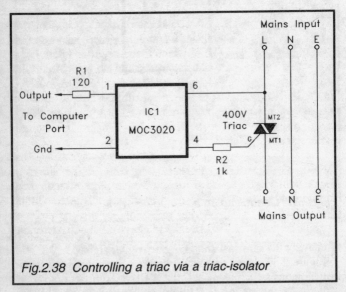

Fig.2.38 Controlling a triac via a triac-isolator

This circuit should work with any normal triac, but should not be used with a triac that has a built-in diac. For 230 volt mains use a triac having a maximum operating voltage rating of at least 400 volts is required (bearing in mind that the peak mains voltage is around 350 volts). The current rating required obviously depends on the application, and the power rating of the load that will be controlled.

Bear in mind that a heatsink will almost certainly be required for currents of about 1 amp or more. For loads of several amps a substantial heatsink will be required as the triac will be dissipating what is likely to be around 10 or 20 watts. Another point to keep in mind is that the heat-tab on many triacs connects internally to one of the terminals (usually MT2). Unless the triac is reliably insulated from the heatsink, the heatsink will also be connected to this terminal (and to the mains supply). **Remember to take all the necessary safety precautions when dealing with any project that connects to the mains supply.**

Simple Opto-Isolator

While on the subject of opto-isolation it is perhaps worth mentioning that it is sometimes necessary to include opto-isolation on digital inputs or outputs of a computer. There are two common reasons for this, one of which is the need for safety isolation when a computer is used in certain medical electronics applications. The biofeedback monitor featured previously is an example of this, but the biofeedback circuit used an analogue coupling. Here we are talking about a simple digital coupling, such as might be required in a heart rate monitor application.

The more common reason for including opto-isolation is that there is a risk of a high voltage existing between the chassis of the computer and the chassis of some other piece of equipment to which it is connected. In my experience this is something that only occurs when neither the computer nor the piece of ancillary equipment have an earthed chassis, but both are mains powered. This will not normally be a problem with a PC, since these all seem to have earthed chassis.

Anyway, if in doubt it is generally best to include isolation, and all that is required is a simple circuit of the type shown in Figure 2.39. This has the usual l.e.d. and current limiting resistor (R1) on the input side, and R2 as the load resistor on the output side. The photo-transistor in IC1 is used as an emitter follower switch. Pin 6 connects to the base terminal of the photo-transistor, but in this circuit no connection is made to the base terminal (there is no internal connection to pin 3 of IC1 incidentally).

Although this circuit is shown as fitting on an output line from the computer, it is quite in order to use it the other way round, with the output of the isolator circuit driving a digital input of the computer. A TIL111 is specified for IC1, but any "bog standard" opto-isolator should work in this circuit.

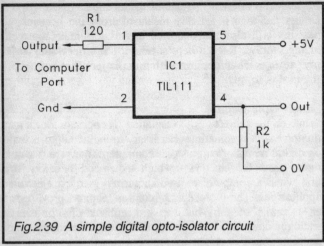

Fig.2.39 A simple digital opto-isolator circuit

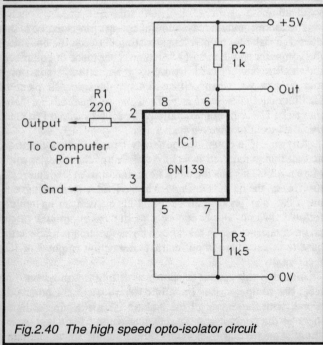

Fig.2.40 The high speed opto-isolator circuit

Multiple opto-isolators are available, and usually represent the cheapest and most convenient means of providing isolation on a number of lines. For example, if isolation is required on all eight bits of a digital port, two quad opto-isolators would probably be the best means of providing the isolation.

When using opto-isolators it is essential to bear in mind that they are very slow devices by electronic standards. Inexpensive types can generally transfer squarewave signals at frequencies of up to a few kilohertz, but at higher frequencies the output fails to switch properly between logic levels. At high frequencies the output signal simply fails to materialise at all. Better results can be obtained using high speed opto-isolators, but most of these are still very slow in comparison to logic circuits.

Figure 2.40 shows the circuit diagram for an opto-isolator based on a 6N139. This has the usual infra-red LED on the input side, but has a photodiode, emitter follower buffer stage, and common emitter switch on the output side. This gives much improved performance, and this circuit can handle squarewave signals at frequencies of up to a few hundred kilohertz. Admittedly, this is still slow by logic circuit standards. On the other hand, it is still adequate for the majority of practical applications. R2 is the load resistor for the emitter follower stage, and R3 is the load resistor for the common emitter output stage.

D.C. Motor Control

Control of a small d.c. electric motor from a computer via a digital to analogue converter is a simple process. It basically just requires some voltage amplification and some high current buffering at the output of the converter. The motor control circuits described here are primarily intended for use as model train controllers, but they can be used to control any d.c. electric motors which have similar power requirements. These circuits are designed to provide a maximum output potential of 12 volts or so at currents of up to one amp. The larger gauge model trains sometimes require a supply current of up to about 2 amps, and these circuits can handle the extra current provided adequate heatsinking is provided for the output transistor, and the power supply circuit has an adequate rating. Note that these circuits require their own mains power supply units, and can not be powered from the PC's supply rails.

Figures 2.41 and 2.42 show the circuit diagram for a controller of the constant voltage variety. A circuit of this type simply supplies the motor with a variable stabilised voltage. The voltage is constant in that it does not vary in sympathy with changes in the current drawn by the motor. The circuit of Figure 2.41 is for the digital to analogue converter. This is basically just the circuit based on the ZN426E that was featured in Chapter 1, but the output amplifier section has been omitted. Instead, the high power amplifier circuit of Figure 2.42 is used.

The output voltage range from the ZN426E digital to analogue converter is 0 to 2.55 volts. The controller circuit must therefore provide a voltage amplification of just under five times in order to convert this into the required 0 to 12 volt output range. IC2 is an operational amplifier used in the non-

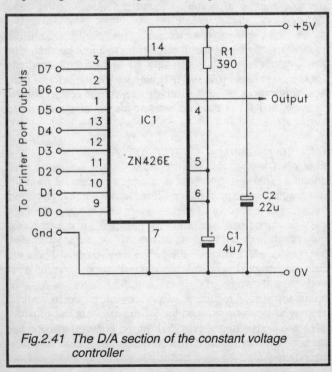

Fig.2.41 The D/A section of the constant voltage controller

150

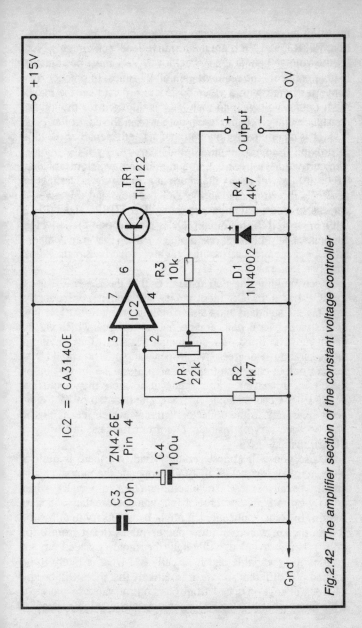

Fig.2.42 The amplifier section of the constant voltage controller

151

inverting mode, and this stage provides the voltage amplification. R2, R3, and VR1, are the negative feedback circuit which set the voltage gain at the correct level. VR1 must be adjusted to give precisely the required gain of 4.7 times. In practice, the converter is fed with a value of 255 in order to set the maximum output voltage, and then VR1 is adjusted for the lowest resistance that gives maximum output from the controller.

TR1 is an emitter follower output stage that enables the unit to provide the high output currents required by a d.c. motor. The current drive from IC1 is quite limited, which means that TR1 must provide a very high current gain. A power Darlington device is therefore used in the TR1 position, and this gives a current gain of a few thousand times. The TIP121 and TIP122 both work well in this circuit. D1 is a protection diode which suppresses any high reverse voltage spikes that might otherwise be generated across the highly inductive load. R4 is simply a load resistor for TR1.

When building the unit remember that the CA3140E used for IC1 has a PMOS input stage, and that it consequently requires the standard anti-static handling precautions. TR1 has to dissipate several watts at most output voltages, which means that it must be fitted on a substantial heatsink. One having a rating of about 5 degrees Celsius per watt (or less) should suffice for output currents of up to 1 amp. For a 2 amp version of the circuit a heatsink with a rating of no more than about 2.5 degrees per Celsius should be used. The heat-tab of TR1 connects internally to the collector terminal, which means that it will be necessary to insulate TR1 from the heatsink using a TO220 insulating kit.

In use you will almost certainly find that there is quite a wide range of low values that fail to operate the motor. This is simply because most d.c. electric motors, especially when heavily loaded, require three or four volts before they will start to turn. In some applications it might be necessary to allow for this in the software, with low output values (apart from 0 for "off") being avoided. Although the motor's speed is not continuously variable and it actually has what is likely to be around 200 different speeds, it is unlikely that there will be any obvious change in speed from one control value to the next. This gives what is effectively a continuously variable speed.

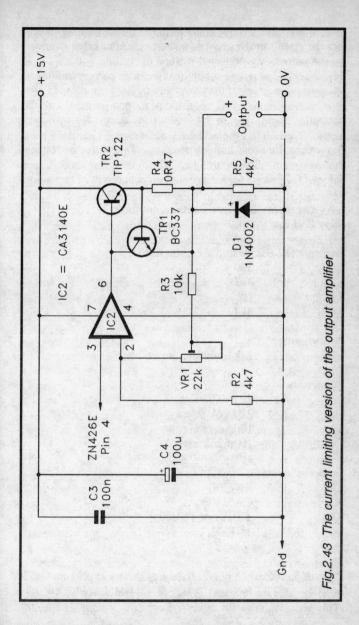

Fig.2.43 The current limiting version of the output amplifier

153

It is advisable to have some form of current limiting to protect the circuit in the event of a short circuit or other overload on the output. My preferred method of dealing with this is to have a regulated power supply that includes current limiting at an appropriate level. If the power supply does not provide suitable current limiting it is not difficult to incorporate it into the controller circuit. Figure 2.43 shows the circuit for an output amplifier which has the necessary additions. TR1 and R4 are a conventional current limiting circuit, and the value of R4 sets the maximum output current at a little over one amp. Use a value of 0.22 ohms for a maximum output current of two amps.

Components for Constant Voltage Controller
(Figs 2.41 and 2.42)

Resistors (all 0.25 watt 5% carbon film)
R1   390
R2   4k7
R3   10k
R4   4k7

Potentiometer
VR1   22k miniature preset

Capacitors
C1   4µ7 63V elect
C2   22µ 16V elect
C3   100n ceramic
C4   100µ 25V elect

Semiconductors
IC1   ZN426E
IC2   CA3140E
TR1   TIP121 or TIP122
D1   1N4002

Miscellaneous
8 pin d.i.l. holder, 14 pin d.i.l. holder, 25 way D plug and lead, heatsink for TR1 (see text), case, circuit board, solder, etc.

Forward/Reverse

The direction of a d.c. electric motor is controlled by the polarity of the applied voltage. In a model train controller application, or any other application that requires direction control via the computer, some switching is needed at the output of the controller. Basically all that is needed is a relay driver and a relay having twin changeover contacts. The latter are wired in the manner shown in Figure 2.44. The contacts must be of the break before make variety, and not the make before break type (which would short circuit the output of the controller on each changeover). All the relays I have ever used have been equipped with break before make contacts, but it is worthwhile checking this point just in case. Of course, if manual switching is required, simply use a DPDT switch instead of relay contacts.

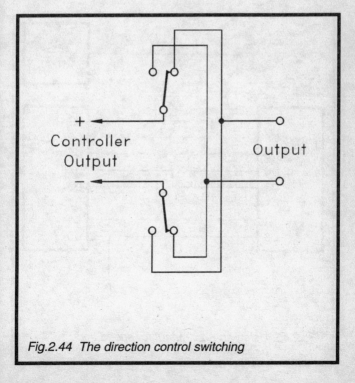

Fig.2.44 The direction control switching

When using a motor speed controller plus the direction control circuit it is obviously necessary to have nine output lines (eight for speed control and one for direction control). There is no major problem when interfacing to a PC printer port, since there are four handshake output lines in addition to the eight normal data outputs. Problems only arise if these lines are needed for other purposes, such as controlling model signals.

It is possible to provide speed and direction control from an eight bit port, but seven bit resolution has to be accepted for the speed control circuit. In practice this will still give something like a hundred different speeds, which provides quite fine speed control. This permits smooth acceleration and deceleration of a model train with no obvious jumping from one speed to the next.

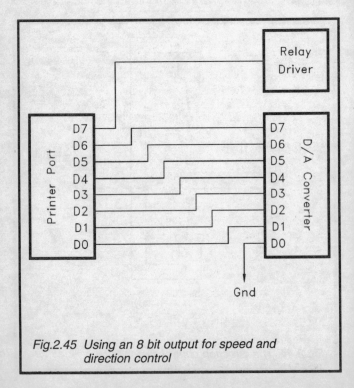

Fig.2.45 Using an 8 bit output for speed and direction control

The basic method of using an eight bit port for both types of control is shown in Figure 2.45. The general scheme of things is to have the lower seven bits of the port drive the upper seven inputs of the digital to analogue converter. There is no output available to drive the least significant input of the converter which is therefore connected to earth. This reduces the maximum output voltage to 2.54 volts, but this is not of any real importance in practice. The most significant output is free for use with the direction control relay driver circuit.

With this system values from 0 to 127 provide speeds from zero to maximum. Adding 128 to a value provides the same speed, but reverses the direction of the motor. For example, 32 provides a low speed in one direction, while 160 (32 plus 128) provides the same speed in the opposite direction. There should be no difficulty in writing software for this method of control.

Software

This simple GW BASIC program provides a basic train controller function. It is written for a controller that uses the eight data outputs to drive the digital to analogue converter, and "Out 2" to provide direction control.

```
10    REM A/D CONVERTER TRAIN CONTROLLER PROGRAM
20    OUT &H378,0
30    OUT &H37A,0
40    CLS
50    PRINT "PRESS '1' TO ACCELERATE"
60    PRINT "PRESS '2' TO SLOW DOWN"
70    PRINT "PRESS '3' TO END"
80    PRINT "PRESS 'F' FOR FORWARDS"
90    PRINT "PRESS 'R' FOR REVERSE"
100   X = 0
110   OUT &H378,X
120   A$ = INKEY$
130   IF LEN(A$) = 1 THEN GOSUB 150
140   GOTO 110
150   IF ASC(A$) = 49 THEN X = X  + 5
160   IF ASC(A$) = 50 THEN X = X – 5
170   IF ASC(A$) = 51 THEN END
180   IF ASC(A$) = 114 THEN OUT &H37A,4
```

```
190  IF ASC(A$) = 102 THEN OUT &H37A,0
200  IF X > 255 THEN X = 255
210  IF X < 0 THEN X = 0
220  RETURN
```

The first few lines simply set the start-up conditions, with the
train stopped and set to the notional forward direction. Lines 40
to 90 print instructions on the screen which tell the user which
keys to press for various actions. Lines 110 to 140 provide a
continuous loop which monitors the keyboard. If a key press is
detected, the program branches to the subroutine at lines 150 to
220. Depending on which key is pressed, the subroutine increments or decrements the value of "X" (the value written to the
converter), alters the direction setting, or brings the program to
a halt. Lines 200 and 210 keep the value of "X" within the
acceptable limits of 0 to 255. The value of "X" is incremented
and decremented by five rather than one per loop, simply
because I found that incrementing and decrementing one at a
time gave very sluggish control. With a fast PC increments and
decrements of one would probably give better results.

One advantage of using a computer for this type of thing is
that sophisticated control can be provided using very basic
hardware. For example, simulated inertia, momentum, and
braking can be implemented by software routines, and do not
require any additional hardware. It is well worthwhile experi-
menting a little with various methods of software control.

Pulsed Controller

On the face of it, a constant voltage controller will provide
perfect results with smooth control of the motor's speed and
consistent results. In practice, results using this type of controller are often not entirely satisfactory. This depends on the
particular application, but for use as a model train controller in
particular, results can be very disappointing in certain respects.
These are the starting and low speed performance.

These problems are not really due to any flaw in the controller, and are largely due to the natural characteristics of small
d.c. electric motors. These motors tend to have a reluctance to
start, so that quite a high voltage must be applied to a d.c. motor
before it will begin to operate. Once started, this voltage is

sufficient to run the motor at quite high speed. Some motors exhibit this phenomenon more than others, but it seems to be present in all d.c. electric motors to a significant degree. In a model train context it gives the "jump start" effect, where instead of starting and accelerating smoothly, the train suddenly jumps to about one-third or even half speed.

At slow speeds there is a tendency for d.c. motors to stall. Having stalled, it then takes "jump starts" to get them going again. This is a major problem in a computer based system which provides fully automatic control, as the computer will not realise that the train has stalled, and will simply continue to provide the stationary train with low power. If a constant voltage controller is used, probably the best solution is to have an "emergency" key on the keyboard. When pressed, this is detected by a software routine which gives a short burst of full power to the motor. This should spur the motor into action again.

A much better way of handling things is to use a more sophisticated controller which utilizes a system that provides better control of the motor. The most simple route to improved starting and low speed performance is to use a pulsed controller. Rather than having a steady d.c. output signal, a pulse width modulated output signal is used. As we saw with the capacitance measuring interface that was described in Chapter 2, by varying the mark-space ratio of a pulsed d.c. signal the average output voltage can be controlled. A 12 volt d.c. electric motor will work perfectly well from a pulsed d.c. signal, but the output must be at a suitable frequency. In practice quite a wide frequency range gives satisfactory results, and anything from a few hertz to a few kilohertz is normally usable.

With a computer based system it is possible to provide pulsed control using some very simple hardware. Basically all that is needed is an amplifier and buffer circuit driven from a digital output of the computer. The computer rather than the hardware generates a pulsed signal having suitable mark-space ratios. Figure 2.46 shows the circuit diagram for a suitable amplifier/buffer stage.

IC1 operates as a voltage comparator having a reference potential of about 1.7 volts fed to its inverting input by R2 and R3. The digital output port drives IC1's non-inverting input.

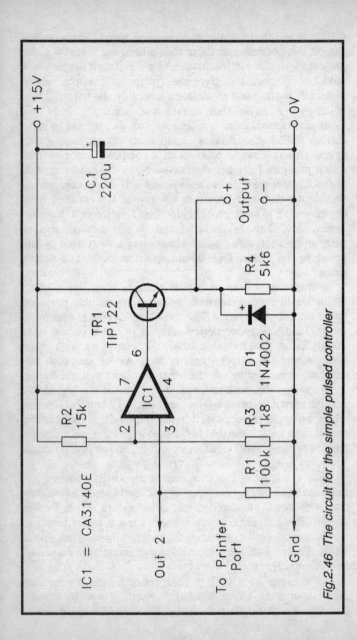

Fig.2.46 The circuit for the simple pulsed controller

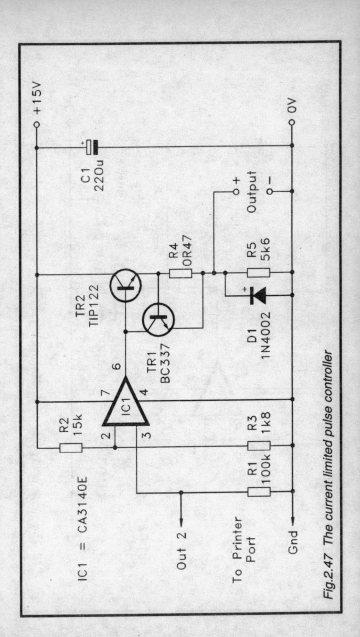

Fig.2.47 The current limited pulse controller

161

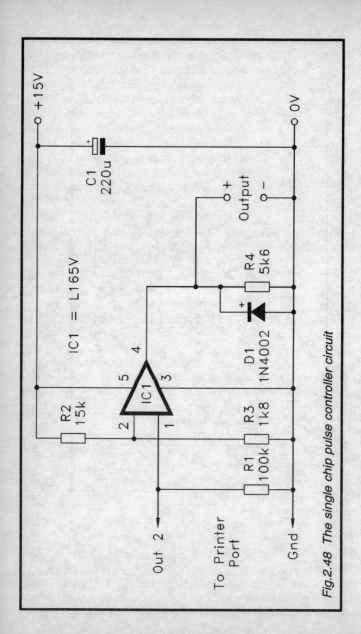

Fig.2.48 The single chip pulse controller circuit

162

R1 provides static protection when the circuit is not connected to the PC. TR1 provides buffering at the output so that high currents required by the motor can be supplied. With the digital output low, the non-inverting input of IC1 will be below the reference level, and the output of the circuit will drop to 0 volts. Taking the digital output high results in the non-inverting input of IC1 going above the voltage at the inverting input, and the output of the circuit then goes to about 12 volts or so.

Figure 2.47 shows the circuit for a simple pulse controller interface that incorporates current limiting. The specified value for R4 sets the maximum output current at just over one amp. Use a value of 0.22 ohms for a maximum output current of two amps. Either way, R4 should have a power rating of 2 watts or more. Figure 2.48 shows the circuit diagram for a pulse controller interface based on an L165V power operational amplifier. This is much the same as the original circuit, but the built-in power amplifier of IC 1 makes a discrete buffer stage unnecessary. One slight drawback of this version is that the low output potential is a volt or so, rather than 0 volts. In practice this does not seem to have a significant effect on performance.

As these circuits are pulse types they produce relatively little dissipation in the output device. However, I would still recommend using a heatsink on the output device. A type having a rating of about 9 degrees Celsius per watt should suffice, but it might be safer to use a slightly larger heatsink (say about 6 degrees Celsius per watt) for a controller that will drive a two amp motor. Incidentally, the heat-tab of the L165V connects internally to pin 3 (the 0 volts supply pin). The heat-tabs of the TIP121 and TIP122 do, of course, connect internally to the collector terminal.

Software

Generating accurate mark-space ratios at a frequency of a few hundred hertz is something that really requires a fairly fast programming language. However, this GW BASIC listing will give reasonable results with a fairly fast PC (at least a 33MHz 80386 processor).

163

```
10    REM PULSED TRAIN CONTROLLER PROGRAM
20    CLS
30    PRINT "PRESS '1' TO ACCELERATE"
40    PRINT "PRESS '2' TO SLOW DOWN"
50    PRINT "PRESS '3' TO END"
60    X = 1000
70    OUT &H37A,4
80    FOR PULSE = 1 TO 100
90    NEXT PULSE
100   OUT &H37A,0
110   FOR PERIOD = 1 TO X
120   NEXT PERIOD
130   A$ = INKEY$
140   IF LEN(A$) = 1 THEN GOSUB 160
150   GOTO 70
160   IF ASC(A$) = 49 THEN X = X – 25
170   IF ASC(A$) = 50 THEN X = X + 25
180   IF ASC(A$) = 51 THEN END
190   IF X > 1000 THEN X = 1000
200   IF X < 1 THEN X = 1
210   RETURN
```

There are two basic approaches to pulse control. The more sophisticated method is to have the mark period decrease as the space period increases, and vice versa. This gives the required changes in average output voltage, but gives a more or less constant output frequency. The more simple method, and the one used here, is to have a fixed mark period, and vary the space time. This still enables a wide range of mark-space ratios to be produced, but gives a broad range of output frequencies.

The FOR . . . NEXT loop at lines 80 and 90 produces the fixed mark ("on") pulse, and loops 100 times. Another FOR …NEXT loop at lines 110 and 120 sets the space ("off") period. This loops the number of times set by variable "X", which is set initially at 1000 (line 60). This gives a mark-space ratio of about 1 to 10, and a low average output voltage. Pressing a key takes the program into the subroutine, and if an appropriate key is pressed, the value of "X" will be stepped up or down in increments or decrements of 25 (lines 160 and 170). Lines 190 and 200 keep the value of "X" between 1 and 1000. This represents an approximate mark-space ratio of 100 to 1 at full power ("X" = 1) to 1 to 10 at minimum power, which is sufficient to give good results with most motors.

It would probably not be too difficult to alter the program to provide variation of both the mark and space times, so as to give less variation in the output frequency. On the other hand, the program works quite well in its current form provided the PC used is reasonably fast.

P.W.M. Control

An alternative method of providing pulsed control is to use a conventional pulse width modulation (p.w.m.) controller, fed from a digital to analogue converter. This type of circuit is controlled in exactly the same way as a constant voltage controller, but the output signal to the motor is a pulsed type.

This method clearly requires more hardware than a software based pulse width controller, and is substantially more expensive to implement. It does have a potential advantage though. This is simply that the computer is not having to use up a large percentage of its time generating an output signal having the correct mark-space ratio. The computer merely outputs values to the digital to analogue converter, and leaves the hardware to generate the appropriate output signal. This permits accurate control using rudimentary software. Furthermore, there is no need to use a fast programming language or a fast PC. Because very little of the computer's processing time is occupied undertaking the basic control of the train, it is possible to undertake sophisticated automatic control of the train. Again, this does not require the use of a fast programming language or the latest thing in go-faster PCs.

Figure 2.49 shows the block diagram for the pulse width modulation controller. The voltage comparator is at the heart of the circuit. It has one input (usually the non-inverting input) fed with the output voltage of the digital to analogue converter. The other input is fed with an attenuated clock signal. It is essential to the operation of the circuit that the clock signal is a reasonably good triangular type. In an application of this type a high degree of linearity through the system is not really needed, so a few imperfections in the clock signal are tolerable.

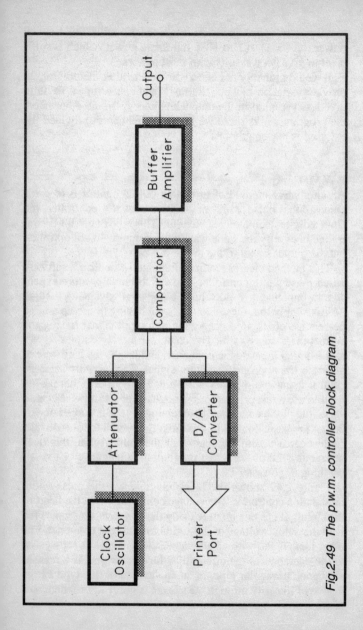

Fig.2.49 The p.w.m. controller block diagram

With zero output voltage from the converter the clock signal will always be at the higher potential, and the output of the comparator will always be low. A small output voltage from the converter will result in the clock signal being at the higher voltage for the majority of the time. The output of the comparator therefore pulses at the clock frequency, but will be low for the majority of the time, giving a low average output voltage. If the output voltage from the converter is increased, the clock signal will be higher than the input voltage for a lesser proportion of the time. This gives a higher average output voltage. If the output voltage of the converter is taken high enough, it will always be higher than the clock voltage, and the output of the comparator will go high continuously.

In practice the attenuator is adjusted so that the maximum and minimum clock voltages are just within the output voltage range of the converter. This enables the average output voltage to be set at zero, the full supply potential, and a wide range of intermediate levels. A buffer amplifier at the output enables the circuit to supply the high output currents required by a small d.c. motor.

P.W.M. Circuit

The digital to analogue converter circuit for the p.w.m. controller is exactly the same as the one for the constant voltage controller (Figure 2.41). The circuit for the rest of the p.w.m. controller appears in Figure 2.50. The clock oscillator is based on IC2, which is a dual operational amplifier. It is used in a conventional triangular/squarewave oscillator of the type which uses an integrator (IC2a) and a trigger circuit (IC2b). In this case only the triangular output signal from IC2a is required. C4 and R4 are the timing components, and these set the clock frequency at around 300 to 400Hz.

The output signal from IC2 has an amplitude of about 9 volts peak-to-peak, which is clearly far larger than the level of about 2.5 volts peak-to-peak needed at the input of the comparator. Also, the minimum clock voltage is about two volts, rather than the required potential of little more than 0 volts. VR1 is used as a variable attenuator which reduces the peak-to-peak amplitude of the clock signal to a suitable figure, and it also reduces the positive offset. D1 to D3 introduce a voltage drop of about 1.8

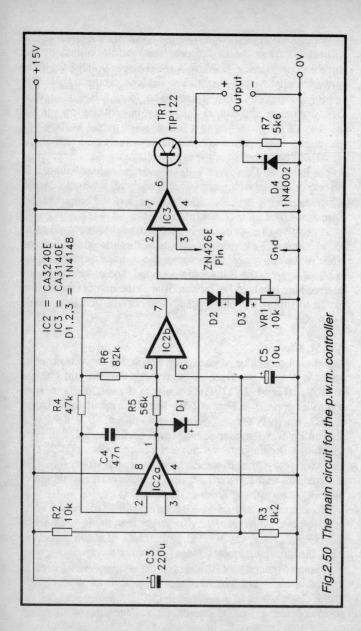

Fig.2.50 The main circuit for the p.w.m. controller

168

volts or so which also helps to take the positive offset down to an acceptable level.

IC3 is an operational amplifier, but in this circuit it functions as the voltage comparator. TR1 is the output buffer stage, and it is a power Darlington device used in the emitter follower mode. R7 acts as its load resistance with no external load connected across the output. D4 suppresses any reverse voltage spikes generated across the highly inductive loading provided by a d.c. electric motor.

Like TR1 in the simple pulsed controller interface, TR1 in this circuit should be fitted with a small heatsink. This circuit is controlled in exactly the same fashion as the constant voltage controller. VR1 must be given a suitable setting if the unit is to work well. Start with the wiper of VR1 at the bottom end of its track. With a value of 255 written to the digital to analogue converter, advance VR1 just far enough to give full speed from the model train. The system should then have a good control characteristic.

Components for P.W.M. Controller (Figs 2.41 and 2.50)

Resistors (all 0.25 watt 5% carbon film)

R1	390R
R2	10k
R3	8k2
R4	47k
R5	56k
R6	82k
R7	5k6

Potentiometer

VR1	10k min preset

Capacitors

C1	4μ7 63V elect
C2	22μ 16V elect
C3	220μ 25V elect
C4	47n polyester
C5	10μ 25V elect

Semiconductors

IC1	ZN426E
IC2	CA3240E
IC3	CA3140E
TR1	TIP121 or TIP122
D1	1N4148
D2	1N4148
D3	1N4148
D4	1N4002

Miscellaneous
8 pin d.i.l. holder (2 off)
14 pin d.i.l. holder
Heatsink for TR1 (see text)
25 way D plug and lead
Case, circuit board, solder, etc.

Mains Power Supply

The PC is unable to provide the +15 volt supply required by the
d.c. motor speed controllers, and the controllers must therefore
have their own built-in mains power supply unit. For the circuits to operate reliably and safely the supply must be reasonably well smoothed and stabilised. A simple power supply unit
such as the one shown in Figure 2.51 is sufficient to drive one
amp versions of the circuits. It will also operate as a two amp
supply provided the current rating of the mains transformer is
at least doubled, FS1 has a rating of 2 amps, and IC1 is a two
amp regulator (such as the RS/Electromail L78S15CV).

The circuit is quite conventional, having full-wave bridge
rectification, smoothing provided by C1, and IC1 to provide
electronic smoothing and regulation. C2 and C3 are decoupling
capacitors which should be mounted close to IC1. They should
then ensure stable operation from IC1. The regulator has built-
in current limiting, which is an important feature in this case.
Overloads and short circuits are common in many motor speed
control applications, especially model train control. Except
where the motor speed control circuit has integral current limiting, it is essential that the power supply circuit fulfils this
function. Either way, the current limiting protects both the

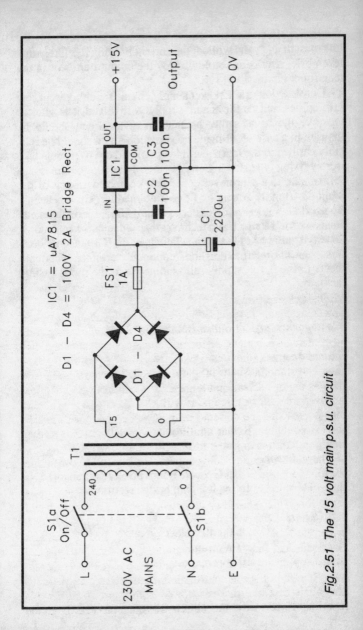

Fig.2.51 The 15 volt main p.s.u. circuit

171

controller circuit and the motor. The controller is probably in the most danger, and without the current limiting it is likely that even brief overloads would destroy the output transistor in the controller circuit.

Construction of the power supply circuit should present few difficulties, but as the mains supply is involved it is vital to observe the usual safety precautions. The circuit should be housed in a case of all-metal construction and it should be reliably earthed to the mains earth lead. The lid or cover must be a screw fixing type, and not one that simply unclips or slides out. Make sure that you never come into contact with any of the mains wiring. IC1 must be fitted on a medium sized heatsink. In practice it is probably easier to simply mount it on the metal case which should provide more than adequate heatsinking. There is no need to use an insulating set on IC1 since its heat-tab connects internally to the "common" terminal. This connects to the 0 volt supply rail (and hence to the metal casing) anyway.

Components for 15V Mains P.S.U. (Fig. 2.51)

Transformer
T1   Mains primary, 15 volt, 1.5 amp
                            secondary

Switch
S1   Rotary on /off mains switch

Semiconductors
IC1   7815 (15 volt 1 amp positive regulator)
D1 – D4   100 volt 2 amp bridge rectifier

Capacitors
C1   2200µ 40V elect
C2   100n ceramic
C3   100n ceramic

Fuse
FS1   20mm 1 amp anti-surge

Output sockets, case, circuit board, heatsink for IC1, solder, etc.

Stepper Motor Driver

A stepper motor is a form of d.c. electric motor, but it is totally different to the motors used to drive model trains, etc. The most important difference is that, as its name implies, a stepper motor is stepped from one position to another. It is used where it is necessary to precisely position something, and not normally used where continuous rotation is required. It would be possible to use a stepper motor to (say) drive a model train, but it would definitely be doing things the hard way, and would provide no obvious advantage. Also, stepper motors tend to have far less power than ordinary electric motors half their size. This somewhat limits their practical use, and is something that needs to be borne in mind when contemplating the use of a stepper motor.

There are actually several types of stepper motor, but the type we are concerned with here is the four phase variety. These motors have four electro-magnets, and they are all powered continuously in use. By altering the polarities of the electro-magnets, the motor can be stepped from one position to the next. Figure 2.52 shows the basic way in which a stepper motor operates. Remembering that unlike poles attract and like poles repel, it can be seen that by switching the polarities of the four electro-magnets in the manner shown, the permanent magnet (the one at the centre, which is free to rotate) can be dragged from one position to the next. By reversing the sequence the magnet can be stepped in the opposite direction.

This setup is quite complex to control in that there are four electro-magnets, and it must be possible to reverse the signal to each one so that its polarity can be reversed. In practice things are simplified by having the four magnetic poles provided by two electro-magnets in a sort of cross formation. This is an acceptable way of doing things since, as can be seen from Figure 2.52, each pole is of the opposite polarity to the one physically opposite to it. A further simplification is to have two anti-phase windings on each electro-magnet. This enables the

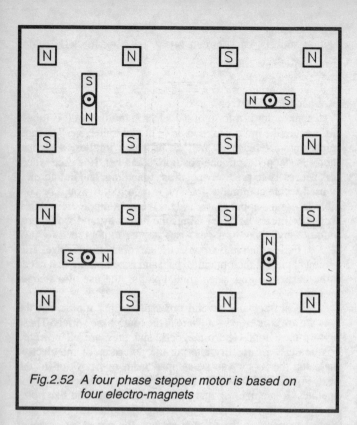

Fig.2.52 A four phase stepper motor is based on
        four electro-magnets

polarity of each electro-magnet to be altered simply by switching from one coil to the other. A real stepper motor therefore has four coils, but only two of the four coils are actually switched on at any one time, and there are still four electro-magnetic poles.

A stepper motor based on this method has a resolution of 90 degrees. While this does not render such a motor of no practical value, control in smaller steps would clearly be an advantage, and make life easier when using stepper motors in many practical situations: "Real life" four phase stepper motors use more electro-magnets and magnetic poles to obtain higher resolution, but retain exactly the same method of control.

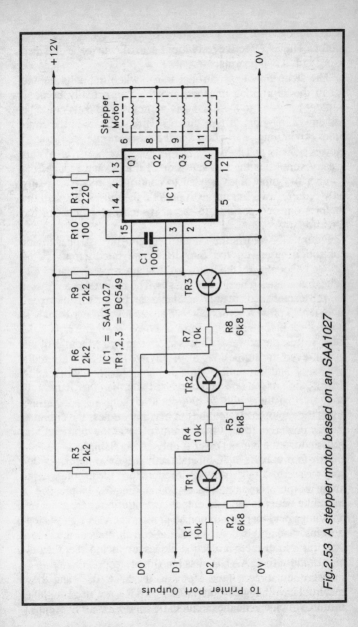

Fig.2.53 A stepper motor based on an SAA1027

175

A resolution of 7.5 or 15 degrees is typical for one of these motors. Higher effective resolutions can, of course, be obtained using step down gearing.

The stepper motor controller must switch the coils on and off in the appropriate manner, and this can actually be done without resorting to a special driver circuit. The coils could be driven via relay driver type circuits, with software in the computer switching the coils in the appropriate sequences. However, it is generally easier to use a special driver as this greatly simplifies the software side of things, and reduces the number of output lines needed to control the motor. It really only requires two lines; one to provide the pulses that step the motor from one position to the next, and one to control the direction of rotation.

Figure 2.53 shows the circuit diagram for a stepper motor controller based on the SAA1027 integrated circuit. This device is not exactly the last word in stepper motor control circuits, but it does have its advantages. The main ones are that it is well established, readily available, and relatively inexpensive. It also provides a perfectly adequate level of performance. It does not incorporate any form of power economy circuit. In other words, the power is always applied to two windings of the motor, even during periods of inactivity. This is not normally necessary, and it is unlikely that the motor position will tend to drift if none of the coils are energised. On the other hand, it is unlikely that there will be any great advantage in powering-down the motor during periods of inactivity unless the circuit is battery powered. In the vast majority of cases the motor will be powered from a mains power supply circuit though.

The four outputs of IC1 can directly drive the stepper motor coils provided they do not require more than the absolute maximum output current rating of 500 milliamps. In practice it would be better to have an output current of no more than 350 milliamps, and there should be no problem here as 12 volt stepper motors mainly seem to operate at coil currents of much less than this. No discrete protection diodes are included at the outputs because the SAA1027 has built-in protection diodes.

There are three control inputs to the SAA1027, and these require 12 volt logic signals. TR1 to TR3 are used as level shifters which enable the circuit to be controlled using ordinary

5 volt logic levels. These stages also provide inversions, but this is of no great practical consequence. The controlling software simply has to be tailored to suit this inverted method of control. In Figure 2.53 the inputs are shown as connecting to the three least significant lines of the printer port data lines, but this is only done as an example of how the circuit can be controlled. Any three outputs will do, and they do not even have to be lines from the same port.

The pulses to step the motor are applied to input D2. The motor is stepped on low to high transitions. As this input is edge triggered, the duration of the input pulses is unimportant. Very short pulses could be missed by the circuit though, and it is probably best to use pulses of no less than a few microseconds in duration. In practice using shorter pulses would not be possible anyway, except by using a very fast computer language on a reasonably fast PC.

A crucial point to keep in mind when designing the control software is that the maximum step frequency is likely to be quite low. The maximum usable frequency will vary from one motor to another, but it will generally be no more than 20 to 30 hertz, and might be much less than this. Although ordinary d.c. electric motors can operate at speeds of up to a few thousand r.p.m., the maximum for a stepper motor could well be no more than a few dozen r.p.m. Remember that these motors are designed for precision control, not for high speed or high power. Some trial and error will be needed to determine the maximum usable speed for a given application, and the software must include delay loops or some other means of ensuring that this pulse rate is never exceeded.

D1 is the direction control input, and with the motor connected to IC1 correctly it will rotate in a clockwise direction with D1 high, and in an anti-clockwise direction when it is low. Input D0 is the reset input, and taking this high resets the four outputs of IC1 to their initial state. Note that this is not the same as taking the motor back to its initial position – it simply resets the outputs to one of their four sets of output states. In a practical application the software normally needs to keep count of the pulses sent to the motor. This can be done using simple software routine to provide a counter action, and a byte or two of RAM to store the answer. The motor's position can then be determined from the value in the counter. If two way operation is used, then pulses to move the motor in one direction must increment the counter, while pulses to move it in the other direction must decrement the counter.

There is a flaw in this system in that it is possible for something to temporarily block the motor so that its true position is out of step with the notional position read from the counter. There is no easy way around this, and a feedback mechanism to check movement of the motor is likely to be far too complex and costly to implement. The only practical course of action is to, as far as possible, make sure that nothing blocks the motor. Also, make sure that there is an easy way of getting things back into synchronisation if things should go wrong. In practical applications there are often micro-switches that detect when the object controlled by the motor has reached either the minimum or maximum limit of its run. This provides the computer with a means of getting the motor to a known position.

It is obviously essential for the stepper motor to be connected correctly if everything is to function correctly. I used a Maplin stepper motor which has colour coded flying leads. These are connected in the manner shown in this table.

Colour	Connection Point
Green	+12V
Green	+12V
Blue	IC1 Q1
Yellow	IC1 Q2
Red	IC1 Q3
White	IC1 Q4

Note that there are only two leads which connect to the +12 volt supply, and not four. This is quite common, and is due to the way that the pairs of windings are wound on each pole piece. Of course, other four phase stepper motors will almost certainly use a different method of coding the leads, but the retailer should provide connection information with any stepper motor.

Components for Stepper Motor Controller (Fig. 2.53)

Resistors (all 0.25 watt 5% carbon film unless noted)

R1	10k
R2	6k8
R3	2k2
R4	10k
R5	6k8
R6	2k2
R7	10k
R8	6k8
R9	2k2
R10	100R
R11	220R 1 watt

Capacitor

C1	100n ceramic

Semiconductors

TR1	BC549
TR2	BC549
TR3	BC549
IC1	SAA1027

Miscellaneous
14 pin d.i.l. IC holder
Four phase stepper motor (Maplin FT73Q or similar)
Circuit board, case, solder, etc.

Notes

Please note following is a list of other titles that are available in our range of Radio, Electronics and Computer books.

These should be available from all good Booksellers, Radio Component Dealers and Mail Order Companies.

However, should you experience difficulty in obtaining any title in your area, then please write directly to the Publisher enclosing payment to cover the cost of the book plus adequate postage.

If you would like a complete catalogue of our entire range of Radio, Electronics and Computer Books then please send a Stamped Addressed Envelope to:

BERNARD BABANI (publishing) LTD
THE GRAMPIANS
SHEPHERDS BUSH ROAD
LONDON W6 7NF
ENGLAND